The Adult ADD
Solution

The Adult ADD Solution

A 30 DAY HOLISTIC ROADMAP TO
OVERCOMING ADULT ADD/ADHD

George Sachs, PsyD

ISBN-13: 9780996950732
ISBN-10: 0996950737
Library of Congress Control Number: 2017912672
Sachs Center, New York City, NY

Introduction

My name is George Sachs. I'm a clinical psychologist and specialist in Adult ADD. I also have Adult ADD, so much of what I teach comes from my own personal experience. I have experimented with many methods on the market with much trial and error. Lots of errors!

I was never satisfied with the books I read on Adult ADD, as the advice was hard to follow and was clearly not created by someone with ADD.

The tools, tips, and techniques I developed for this book, and the accompanying thirty-day, online-learning program have been field tested by me and my clients. With great success.

Why did I make the program only 30 days long? Of course, you can't cure Adult ADD, and certainly not in thirty days. But in thirty days, you will receive a road map to change. This program is just the beginning of a lifetime of learning about your unique symptoms. In thirty days you will learn what critical areas of your life need more attention.

Many of my clients have tried medication, hoping for a miracle to cure their worst symptoms. The truth is, medication can be effective for some, but most of my clients stop taking it because of the side effects—and then where are they? No better off than when they first started. That is why I coach them that they need to learn tools and new techniques to better manage their lives with Adult ADD. That is what this program does—offers thirty days of holistic, actionable advice that can be implemented immediately. With no negative side effects!

I believe in a holistic approach that starts with sleep, diet, and exercise, and that includes emotional, relational, and spiritual practices to truly overcome Adult ADD. This book deals with more than just tips to become more organized. We examine the impact of a life of untreated Adult ADD and how that affects self-esteem, relationships, and overall success. The key word is "overall." That is our holistic approach, because Adult ADD affects all areas of one's life.

How many times have you bought a paper date planner hoping that this time you would actually use it? I know that the normal advice many so-called experts give to adults with ADD just doesn't work. Maybe because those experts don't have Adult ADD. Well, I do. So I know that the typical methods for organization and productivity don't always work for us adults with ADD. That is why I offer work-arounds. These are field-tested tools, tips, and techniques that work for adults with ADD and take into account the unique way that we approach life. I hope that you find the concepts I teach equally helpful and easy to understand. Adult ADD is challenging for oneself and loved ones, but with support and this program, you can overcome some of your worst symptoms and become the person you always knew you could be.

George Sachs PsyD.

DAY 1
Sleep

*I get a second wind around 10:00 p.m.
each night and then start doing things
that keep me up until past midnight. I'm
exhausted each day but can't seem to get
myself to bed at a reasonable hour. Help!*
—TERRY, KENTUCKY

Do you turn on your computer—or phone—at 10:30 p.m. and start surfing the web? Maybe you decide to jump into a massive spring cleaning project right before going to bed. Or perhaps you are like me, a night owl who is just getting started when the sun goes down.

Getting to bed on time is a chronic challenge for adults with ADD. The consequences of this habit can be devastating, which is why proper sleep hygiene is one of the first lessons of our Adult ADD program.

The science is clear. Sleep debt or sleep deficit impairs cognition, executive functioning, attention, and working memory.

In fact, the result of sleep deprivation mirrors the symptoms of Adult ADD, which may cause you to wonder if you have Adult ADD or chronic sleep deprivation.

The answer is often both. The impulsivity and procrastination of Adult ADD often cause adults to stay up later, leading to reduced sleep. This sleep debt makes the existing symptoms of Adult ADD much worse.

It's a chicken-and-egg story. But, in this case, the chicken is exhausted, living on caffeine and only five hours of sleep a night.

While all adults should be aware of the effects of sleep deprivation, this is particularly true for those with ADD. As stated, poor sleep exacerbates the already debilitating symptoms of Adult ADD.

Many adults with ADD get into the habit of staying up too late, surfing the web, and checking e-mails or Facebook without considering the consequences for tomorrow. If you're like me, there's always one more episode of your current binge on Netflix to watch before going to bed. Before you know it, it's 1:00 a.m., and you have to be up in five hours. And then you wonder why you can't focus during morning meetings.

So what can you do to get more sleep and stop the chronic pattern of sleep deprivation and "enhanced Adult ADD"?

One strategy I suggest to my clients is to start thinking about bedtime much earlier in the evening. Doing so teaches you that going to bed is a choice that can be controlled. This may sound easy, but most adults with ADD don't think about sleep until three minutes before their heads hit the pillow.

Sometimes I hear clients complain that they don't feel tired until they're literally about to pass out. I believe this is true for those with ADD, and I know it's true for me. If you're checking Facebook every ten minutes before bed, your brain will not get the signal that you're tired. Too much other information is coming in and being processed for that message to get across.

To counteract the effects of information overload, you need to train yourself to start looking at the clock and begin winding down at a certain time, regardless of how awake you feel. "Winding down" is the total time it takes to get ready for bed, including shutting off screens, getting undressed, washing your face or brushing your teeth. Once you figure out the time you'll need, add thirty minutes to that number.

Why so much time? Those with ADD procrastinate and get derailed from the things they have to do, which, in this case, is going to bed. Generally, I recommend one hour to wind down. For instance, if you want to be in bed by 11:30 p.m., you need to begin to wind down one full hour earlier. The best way to develop this habit is to set an alarm at 10:30 p.m. that signals the wind-down time has begun.

There is another advantage to ditching the screens at an earlier hour. Research shows that close proximity to a bright computer or smartphone screen activates the pineal gland, which controls the amount of melatonin in your body. Melatonin influences biological rhythms, including sleep. Staring at a computer or cell phone for hours before bed fools the brain into thinking that the sun is shining brightly and it's time to wake up and start the day. The problem is that in the real world it's bedtime.

Based on these simple concepts, I tell my clients that if they can limit distractions after 10:30 p.m., particularly smartphone and computer usage, they are halfway to making significant improvements. It's not easy, and it could take some practice, but formulating new habits always takes time.

To create the habit of winding down one hour before bedtime, get an old-fashioned wall calendar. Cross off each night you were able to start the wind-down process at 10:30 p.m. and get into bed by 11:30 p.m. See how many days in a row you can manage. Make it fun, and try to extend your streak one more night than you were able to do before. Within a few weeks of this game, a new habit will be formed.

To review, here is the five-step sleep formula for adults with ADD. These recommendations offer a series of steps you can take to create a more consistent and effective sleep routine. First, establish a sleep schedule and stick to it. As mentioned, the schedule begins one hour before bedtime. I suggest a bedtime of 11:30 p.m. at the latest, as it might take up to a half hour to fall asleep. It is important to keep not only the same bedtime but also the same wake-up time, even on weekends. The pattern of consistent bedtime and rising time regulates the body's internal time clock.

Second, going to bed is not like jumping off a cliff. Moving from frenetic activity to sleep is difficult for anyone, but for adults with ADD this task is nearly impossible. Instead, create a relaxing wind-down routine as a smooth transition from your daytime activities to sleep. In addition to an alarm to remind you to wind down, you can also set some of the house lights to go off an hour before bedtime using a smartphone app and Philips Hue light bulbs.

Exercising during the day is the third step in creating a more stable sleep cycle. Exercise helps rid the body of excess nervous energy and sets off powerful endorphins, which create a sense of overall relaxation and foster improved focus and concentration. There's one caveat, however. Do not exercise in the evening if doing so will come at the expense of your sleep.

Fourth, ask yourself if the environment of your bedroom is conducive to relaxation and sleep. Many people like to keep their bedrooms warm and cozy, especially in the winter. The truth, however, is that slightly cooler temperatures promote better sleep. Bedroom temperatures should be between sixty-five and seventy-one degrees. Your bedroom should also be free from any noise or light that might disturb your sleep. This includes snoring from your partner. (You may have to temporarily institute different accommodations.) Adding blackout curtains, eye shades, ear plugs, and even white noise machines can all help transform your bedroom from a distracting space into one that does what it is designed to do—produce sleep.

The fifth and final step is to ensure that your mattress and pillows are comfortable and supportive. Many younger adults often ignore this rule, assuming that they are healthy and fit, and do not need extra "help" from a mattress. However—regardless of age—you should take advantage of the many new comfortable bedding products that are available. I myself have spent hours looking for the perfect pillow at the local bed and bath store.

If these steps do not immediately solve your sleeping difficulties, do not give up. Many people with ADD have built up a lifetime of bad sleeping habits, and it can take several weeks or even months before the body becomes attuned to a different routine. If you find yourself having difficulty falling asleep, do not lie in bed ruminating about why you are not falling asleep. Instead, researchers advise people to get out of bed for a short period of time and engage in a quiet activity to refocus the brain toward relaxation, such as light reading or having a cup of chamomile tea.

As with any change of habit, a big part of a person's success comes from the decision to make the change, as well as having the right tools and strategies in place. Willpower without tools will not work, just as tools and suggestions will not work without a decision to create change. As you progress in your determination to mitigate the effects of ADD, taking control of your sleep habits will yield many positive results.

Daily Checklist

1. Set an alarm at 10:30 p.m. to wind down before bed.

Take Our Quiz

What is the best way to develop a better sleep cycle?

a) Begin a spring cleaning project right before bed.
b) Around 10:30 p.m., start binging on your favorite Netflix series.
c) Set an alarm clock to go off at 10:30 p.m., reminding you to wind down for the night.

Correct Answer: c

DAY 2
Water

et's say it's 8:30 a.m. or maybe 2:30 p.m., and you are feeling sluggish, exhausted, or just out of steam. What is your first reaction?

a. Grab a quick coffee or a 5-hour ENERGY shot.
b. Grab a quick Snickers bar or other candy.
c. Drink a glass of water.

If you're one of the 10.5 million American adults who struggle with Adult ADD, I am willing to wager that your first reaction is probably a or b. Generally, option c, drinking a glass of water, is not part of your daily plan. After all, most people with Adult ADD are not thinking about dehydration and its effects on concentration and other important brain functions. Most likely, they're thinking about gaining some energy—fast.

However, both research and anecdotal evidence suggest that a well-hydrated brain is a well-functioning brain. I found this out personally almost by accident. I was often fatigued, both at home and at the office, until I added a water dispenser at both locations. I quickly became aware of a noticeable change in my level of energy, focus, and powers of concentration—all because I added more water into my daily routine.

The mind-rejuvenating effects of water should not come as a surprise to anyone who has been outside on a hot day and felt sluggish and tired. The difference is that most of us don't recognize that the effects of dehydration don't just happen in the great outdoors. Often offices and homes can get very dry in the winter, leading to that familiar feeling of dry mouth. Dehydration can occur anywhere and anytime when ample water consumption is lacking from a person's daily routine.

It can be difficult to know if you're only slightly dehydrated and functioning at less than your best. By the time the body's thirst mechanism kicks in, you may be a bit dehydrated already. In fact, studies show that as many as two-thirds of Americans are walking around dehydrated and need to drink more water. Regarding symptoms of dehydration, be on the lookout for fatigue, mood swings, hunger despite having eaten recently, achy joints, and dark urine and/or constipation.

What do studies tell us about dehydration and brain function? To date most research on this topic involves children, but the findings are significant for adults as well. In one study, forty children around eight years old were tested on their memory and attention skills. On the first day of testing, the children were allowed frequent trips to the water fountains, and some carried water bottles. In addition, water was given at lunch between 12:00 and 1:00 p.m. and later at 2:30 p.m. Testing occurred twenty to fifty minutes afterward. On the second day, no water was allowed to be consumed. Test results were significantly better on the first day when water was consumed compared to the day of no water at all.

In another study, fifty-eight children between seven and nine years old were divided into two groups. One group was given water; the other was not. Testing twenty minutes after most of the water had been consumed resulted in better attention and memory scores, revealing that mild dehydration in children can impair cognition. Finally, in a class of twenty-three seven-year-olds, a study was conducted on eleven children who received water and twelve who did not. Those who drank water rated themselves happier. Furthermore, attention was better in those who consumed water.

If you have Adult ADD, you already know that your brain needs all the help it can get to keep you on track, and if your productivity, cognition, and mood drop due to dehydration, this becomes a significant issue. With this in mind, I strongly urge my clients to make sure they hydrate often. However, it takes more than simply going to the sink to grab an extra glass of water twice a day, which generally does not work because those extra cups of water are not part of a routine. Research shows that for a change to take effect, it has to become part of a daily routine.

Here are a few suggestions I offer my clients to help them build a routine around increasing their hydration:

- Instead of your regular morning cup of coffee, switch to tea (less of a diuretic). I recommend Sweet and Spicy tea from Good Earth.

- Buy a water dispenser (e.g., Poland Spring), and put it near the TV at home or near your desk if you own your office. The sight of the cold water will motivate you to drink more water. And the cost is only a few extra dollars per month.

If you aren't your own boss (yet) and can't install a water dispenser, make it a habit to fill a BPA-free water bottle every morning and sip from it all day. Add a vitamin powder to make it taste better.

Adult ADD is a multifaceted challenge that requires a multifaceted approach. In my opinion, researchers and therapists have allowed themselves to rely on medication as the sole answer to ADD for far too long. The human brain is an elegant organ that is capable of amazing growth, plasticity, and recovery. Medical traditions dating back thousands of years have encouraged people to take advantage of the benefits of natural foods, herbs, and activities to create inner calm and to improve cognition. Water is one of the most abundant and cheap resources at our disposal. The human body is two-thirds water. Our brains are even more saturated with water, at about 75 percent. That simple fact alone should be enough to encourage you to get in the habit of drinking more water.

Daily Checklist

1. Set an alarm at 10:30 p.m. to wind down before bed.
2. Buy a water dispenser, and place it nearby to increase water consumption.

Take Our Quiz

What is the recommended way to increase water intake?

a) Buy a cold and hot water dispenser, and place it nearby for easy filling.
b) Water is everywhere. I'll drink it when I see it.
c) Drink Red Bull. That has water in it.

Correct Answer: a

DAY 3
Diet

I grew up on a diet of pizza, soda, Chinese food, and McDonald's. Am I proud of this? Well, it was fun while it lasted, and in hindsight, it probably lasted a lot longer than it should have. The problem was that I didn't see the benefits of changing my diet. I wasn't sick or gaining weight, and I generally thought everything was fine. All of this added up to a dietary lifestyle that essentially consisted of grabbing a handful of whatever was easiest and tastiest at the time. Even after I was diagnosed with Adult ADD, I continued to eat like a teenager scavenging through a convenience store.

Full disclosure: Despite my role as a therapist working with Adult ADD, I only woke up to the impact of food on my brain within the last few years. It took a while, and I did not give up my old habits easily. Eventually, though, the more I learned about nutrition, the more disgusted I felt by the garbage I was putting in my body.

My dietary evolution started with documentaries on Netflix. The first was *Super Size Me*, which chronicled certain practices used by the McDonald's corporation to deliberately manipulate customers into ordering unnecessarily large portions of their foods. The backlash generated by this documentary actually forced the fast-food giant to begin offering healthier options on its menu. Even so, for most adults with ADD, the temptation to grab what's easy, fast, and filling makes places like McDonald's the wrong choice almost all of the time.

Next came *Forks Over Knifes* and *Food, Inc.* Both films examine the profound claim that most, if not all, of the degenerative diseases that afflict us can be controlled, or even reversed, by rejecting our present menu of animal-based and processed foods.

The following is a comprehensive list of movies that I believe to be important viewing for adults with ADD:

- *Super Size Me.* As I noted, this documentary has become a classic and documents the effects of a thirty-day all-McDonald's diet.
- *King Corn.* Two friends move to Iowa to become corn farmers and learn some surprising facts about this staple crop.
- *Food Matters.* This movie explores the nutritional and healing benefits of unprocessed foods as well as the negative effects of processed foods and pesticides. The influence of the pharmaceutical industry on the nation's health is also brought into focus.
- *Food, Inc.* This Academy Award–nominated film examines corporate farming in the United States, concluding that agribusiness produces food that is unhealthy, environmentally harmful, and abusive of both animals and employees.

- *Forks Over Knives.* The vegan food movement, including the results of *The China Study* and work that doctors like Dr. Caldwell Esselstyn are doing to reverse heart disease using meatless diets, is explored.
- *GMO OMG.* Jeremy Seifert takes his family on a cross-country, GMO-fact-finding mission that calls attention to how ubiquitous GMO crops have become and what that means for farmers, consumers, and the environment.
- *Lunch Hour.* This movie provides an inside view of the unhealthy lunches being served to our nation's schoolchildren.
- *Fresh.* Rather than sounding the alarm about poor food products, this documentary focuses on how people can build new, healthier dietary habits.
- *Vegucated.* Three meat- and dairy-eating New Yorkers attempt to follow a strict vegan diet for six weeks.
- *Simply Raw: Reversing Diabetes in 30 Days.* In this movie, Dr. Gabriel Cousens challenges six Americans suffering from diabetes to do away with sugar, alcohol, dairy, meat, and other processed items and to take on a 100 percent organic, raw, vegan diet.

If you are having trouble improving your diet, my advice is to make it a project to watch some or all of these documentaries. If you are anything like me, you will begin to see that the American diet needs a serious overhaul. If a bad diet can present so many challenges to the physical and emotional wellbeing of adults without ADD, imagine the kind of havoc our Western way of eating wreaks on the ADD brain and body.

After learning more about the food industry, I began to delve into the science of how food affects the brain. One book I highly recommend is *Grain Brain: The Surprising Truth about Wheat, Carbs, and Sugar—Your Brain's Silent Killers* by David Perlmutter, MD, with Kristin Loberg. The main thesis of this book is that modern forms of wheat are causing all sorts of brain problems ranging from insomnia and headaches to anxiety and depression to epilepsy, schizophrenia, and ADHD.

Another useful book is *The Paleo Manifesto: Ancient Wisdom for Lifelong Health* by John Durant. Drawing from science, culture, anthropology, and philosophy, this book suggests that humans thrive when we live as close to how we lived 10,000 years ago.

For those who prefer not to adopt a Paleo routine, I suggest the Whole30 diet. As with other current research, the Whole30 plan notes that certain foods, such as sugar, grains, dairy, and legumes, may have a negative impact on health and fitness. The plan challenges people to embark on a thirty-day dietary "reset." By cutting out all the unhealthy, gut-disrupting, inflammatory foods for a full 30 days, this diet allows the body to heal and recover from the impact of processed foods. Buy the Whole30 book, *The Whole30: The 30-Day Guide to Total Health and Food Freedom*.

The final book I highly recommend is *The Zone Diet*. Pioneered by Dr. Barry Sears, *The Zone Diet* focuses on balancing blood-sugar glucose levels, which is integral to controlling the willpower that is often lacking in adults with ADD. Scientists at Florida State University found that restoring glucose to a healthy levels typically improves self-control, and that self-control itself appears highly susceptible to glucose. This was echoed by Russell

Barkley, PhD, who was one of the early researchers to focus on Adult ADD as a problem of self-control. Maintaining healthy levels of glucose in the body may improve self-control and ADD symptoms. The US Olympic team hired Dr. Sears to share the Zone Diet with their athletes to maximize performance. Dr. Sears found that a diet rich in protein, low in carbs, and full of healthy vegeables would restore healthy glucose levels and reduce the glucose spikes common in other diets. Maintaining healthy glucose levels allowed the athletes to focus more on training and keep their energy and motivation levels at peak performance.

Do you have to adopt the diet of an Olympic athlete to begin to control some of the symptoms of Adult ADD? Of course not. However, I would point out that if world-class athletes recognize the benefits of improving their diet and nutrition, it's probably good enough for us ordinary folks with Adult ADD. My advice? Get a little smarter about your diet. Your brain will thank you. Your body will thank you. Your boss and your significant other will thank you, too.

Daily Checklist

1. Set an alarm at 10:30 p.m. to wind down before bed.
2. Buy a water dispenser, and place it nearby.
3. Read *The Zone Diet* by Barry Sears to learn how to regulate glucose levels.

Take Our Quiz

Which book teaches you to manage glucose levels to support ADD symptoms?

a) *Eat Pray Love*
b) *Like Water for Chocolate*
c) *The Zone Diet* by Dr. Barry Sears

Correct Answer: c

DAY 4
Exercise

My great aunt lived to be almost one hundred years old. What was her secret to longevity? Three simple rules: Stop eating when you're full. Go to sleep when you're tired. Walk every day.

Sound too simple to be true? It's not. The truth is that research has caught up with my great aunt. The latest studies show that when we exercise, our bodies release chemicals that improve mood and cognitive functioning. In fact, exercise has been touted as being just as effective as Prozac in combating depression and other mood disorders.

When you exercise, your brain releases chemicals called neurotransmitters, including dopamine, which help with attention and focus. People with ADD often have less dopamine in the synapses of their brain, which is one of the reasons staying on task can be so difficult. The bottom line is that if you're not exercising, you're not taking care of your Adult ADD.

I think we all agree that exercise is good for us, but then why don't we all do it? The answers I hear from clients are pretty similar.

"It's too hard."

"It's too boring."

"It's too time-consuming."

Truth be told, starting and maintaining an exercise routine for anyone, let alone someone with ADD, is very hard. It can be boring. It is time-consuming. And it can feel nearly impossible to find the right types of exercise that work with the ADD personality.

To improve the chances of success, I recommend a five-step process for ensuring your exercise program takes hold.

Step one: Find an activity that excites you. Motivation is a problem for adults with ADD, which is why it's important to increase motivation for exercise by finding something that is new and interesting. This could be a dance class, a team activity, or perhaps an extreme sport. In my younger years, knowing I needed exercise to maintain my equilibrium, I took Brazilian dance classes and joined a flag football team, both of which were interesting activities for me.

Step Two: Find an exercise that's easy to start. I was out of shape and needed to find an exercise routine that was interesting and easy to start. I took my aunt's advice and started walking. It was very easy to begin, and I could do it anywhere. Today, I walk ten thousand steps, Monday through Friday, which translates to about five miles. I bought a pedometer to wear on my wrist that shows my steps and motivates me to keep walking when tired. Others may say this is not enough cardio, but it's a simple, accessible exercise that interests me and gets me moving. Walking also gives me the side benefit of getting out into nature, which has a calming effect. Finally, I get some "reading" done on my walks through listening to books on Audible.com.

Step Three: Build exercise into your routine. For a habit to take hold, it must be part of your daily routine. I started walking to work, which has now become a habit. Others fit exercise into their routines by going to the gym during lunch or running on the treadmill first thing in the morning. Regardless, do the activity the same time each day to build consistency and habit.

Step Four: Make it social. Research supports the idea that when doing an activity with others, motivation is higher. Joining a class or a running group will enhance your external motivation to show up each day. The group will also push you further than you thought possible. This theory also applies to hiring a trainer at the gym, who can help keep you motivated and accountable. Walking is not social, but I talk with people all day as a psychologist, so being alone is a nice reward for myself.

Step Five: Reward yourself. The book *The Power of Habit: Why We Do What We Do in Life and Business* by Charles Duhigg describes how adding a reward to a routine can cement the habit-formation process. At the midpoint of my daily walk, I grab a cup of coffee at my favorite coffee stand in the park. This small reward motivates me to begin the walk each day. Find a reward that you can gift yourself at the conclusion of your workout. Maybe it's a smoothie or a nice salad.

Exercise is a key foundational element in the treatment of Adult ADD. So, again, to overcome the boredom and frustration of maintaining an exercise routine, keep these five key elements in mind when picking an exercise program:

1. Find something that excites you.
2. Make it easy to start.
3. Build the activity into your daily routine.
4. Make it social.
5. Reward yourself after each exercise session.

Daily Checklist

1. Set an alarm at 10:30 p.m. to wind down before bed.
2. Buy a water dispenser, and place it nearby.
3. Read the *The Zone Diet* by Barry Sears to learn how to regulate glucose levels.
4. Find an exercise plan that is interesting, easy to start, and social.

Take Our Quiz

What is the most effective exercise program?

a) Tedious, but your abs will look great
b) Easy to start, interesting, and social
c) Requires expensive equipment

Correct Answer: b

DAY 5
Medication

Americans tend to like quick fixes, especially when it comes to anything related to health and well-being. And often the fix we're looking for comes in the form of a pill. Our hope is that, somewhere, groups of scientists are cooking up the perfect medication to cure whatever ails us.

Whether it's cancer, the common cold, or Adult ADD, we love the idea of finding something we can take once a day that works instantaneously and allows us to go on with rest of our lives.

While there is a ton of research from pharmaceutical companies that shows the effectiveness of their ADHD drugs, I don't believe medication is the best way to manage and treat Adult ADD. I'm sure many psychiatrists would disagree, especially if they are on a pharmaceutical company's payroll as a paid speaker. For more on the connection between Big Pharma and the overprescription of ADHD medications, read *ADHD Nation: Children, Doctors, Big Pharma, and the Making of an American Epidemic* by *New York Times* journalist Alan Schwarz.

While medicine can be an effective adjunct to adult-ADD coaching and therapy, the major unspoken problem with ADD medication is that most adults stop taking their pills after six months. Even with all of the advantages associated with medications like Adderall and Concerta, most adults discontinue their prescriptions. But why is this?

The research found a number of reasons, which included a lack of effectiveness, social stigmas, adverse side effects, and the inconvenience of having to take medicine every day. I also often hear from clients that taking medication reinforced the belief that something was wrong with them—that they were somehow damaged—a feeling that became intolerable and was easily remedied by stopping the medicine.

In my practice, I tell clients up front that, statistically, the odds of them discontinuing their medicine is very high. And, without therapy or coaching, they will be no wiser in managing their ADD. I strongly suggest that adults with ADD engage in coaching or therapy, in addition to medication, to learn different ways to manage symptoms. After a few years, their pills may be long gone, but the knowledge they learned will stay forever.

Here are a few personal reactions from adults who responded to an online request on ADDitudemag.com regarding medication.

> "My medication does not work consistently. I am seeing a therapist to improve my behavior. No medication makes ADHD go away."
> —LYNETT, NORTH CAROLINA

"Medication is not always the answer. It does not consistently improve my executive function skills. My doctor has tried different meds, but, so far, the results have been mixed."
—NORMAN, CALIFORNIA

"My meds do not work as well as they used to. I'm post-menopausal now, and I suspect that hormonal changes lessen the effectiveness of the meds."
—RUTH, MINNESOTA

"My ADHD medication doesn't 'fix' everything, though. In addition to seeing a psychiatrist, I work with an excellent therapist, who specializes in cognitive behavioral therapy."
—D. W., VIRGINIA

With all that said, I don't want my readers—or clients—to think that I am antimedication. Nothing could be farther from the truth. However, I do want to make sure that people understand that when it comes to Adult ADD, medication is just one piece of the treatment puzzle. Medication does help with certain symptoms associated with Adult ADD; however, studies show that the adult response to most ADD medications is significantly lower than that of children. One study found that between 25 percent and 78 percent of adults responded positively to medication, compared to between 77 percent and 98 percent of children. These findings led researchers to conclude that a more effective, comprehensive treatment for Adult ADD, including behavioral strategies, was needed to address the executive dysfunction of Adult ADD.

In my own experience with clients, I find that medication can work wonders in terms of helping a person focus, increase motivation, and maintain a sustained effort on less interesting tasks. However, I agree with the researchers in their assertion that medication, over the long haul, cannot help a person become more organized, arrive on time to meetings, or reduce impulsive decision making. Even with all of the advantages associated with medication, if that is your only strategy, you won't even make it through the first year.

Another hidden complication in treating Adult ADD is that many people who participate in therapy for ADD are often dealing with other challenges. Up to 80 percent of adults with ADD also have other disorders, such as depression, bipolar disorder, anxiety, and substance abuse. It is often these coexisting challenges that bring adults with ADD into therapy, rather than their ADD symptoms alone. A lifetime of dealing with the fallout of ADD can leave people with low self-esteem, a sense that they are not capable or competent, or that they are simply "lazy." I have yet to find a pill that can overcome a lifetime of negative messages absorbed from parents, teachers, bosses, and spouses.

While I support medication and believe it can be effective for certain cases, the best treatment involves therapy and gaining a deeper awareness of when, why, and how your symptoms occur. Once you get a handle on the circumstances that trigger certain symptoms or behaviors, tools can be learned and implemented to help you better manage your life as an adult with ADD.

Daily Checklist

1. Set an alarm at 10:30 p.m. to wind down before bed.
2. Buy a water dispenser, and place it nearby.
3. Read *The Zone Diet* by Barry Sears to learn how to regulate glucose levels.
4. Find an exercise plan that is interesting, easy to start, and social.
5. Medication can work for focus and attention, but therapy or coaching is the best long-term solution.

Take Our Quiz

Why is medication not the best solution for Adult ADD?

a) Your teenage son might steal it and sell it at school.
b) Most people discontinue taking their medicine after six months.
c) Wait. What? I thought medication is the magic pill!

Correct Answer: b

Day 6 & 7: Weekend Review

Sleep

Set a timer to remind you to begin the wind-down process one full hour before your desired bedtime to make sure you are calm and relaxed right before bed. Take a hot shower, use black-out shades, and ensure that you have a cool room and comfortable bedding so you can fall asleep and stay asleep.

Water

Buy a water dispenser to make cold water available at all times. Drink water as part of an existing routine. Drink tea to hydrate and stay awake instead of coffee, which can dehydrate you.

Diet

Read *The Zone Diet* and learn how glucose spikes from high-carb diets negatively impact cognition and willpower—two important factors in ADD. Eat more lean meat and learn about the Whole30 Diet.

Exercise

Develop a simple exercise plan that is social, interesting, and easy to accomplish. Increase your level of exercise once your habit is regularly is formed. Walking is good exercise.

Medication

Meet with a psychiatrist to discuss medication. But don't rely on that alone. Find a good therapist or coach who can work with you on behavioral changes.

DAY 8
Self-Regulation and Impulsivity

*How can I stop myself from doing things I don't
want to do? It's like I'm totally at the mercy of
my impulses. Is this because of my ADD?*
—MEGAN, MANHATTAN

As a specialist in Adult ADD and someone who has ADD myself, I understand the challenges that come with this diagnosis. I also know that the traditional methods of treatment may not work. That is why I offer a different take on old problems. This is the genesis of the thirty-day Adult ADD Solution.

One area where new thinking is needed is with impulsive behavior. You don't have to have Adult ADD to act impulsively. But it is also true that one of the hallmarks of Adult ADD is the ongoing, recurrent failure of impulse control, which seeps into almost every area of life.

Russell Barkley, PhD, a top researcher of Adult ADD, calls ADD/ADHD a self-regulation disorder. We know what we need to do, but getting ourselves to do it is a problem. In our quest to stay on task or to adhere to a goal, such as avoiding sugar, we lose focus and act impulsively – we eat the cake. And it's not just overeating or indulging in sweet foods that tempts us. Adults with ADD often shop impulsively, drive impulsively, spend impulsively, speak impulsively, and engage in impulsive sexual behavior. It's no wonder that some scientists believe that as much 25 percent of the prison population has Adult ADD.

Adult ADD is less about attention and focus, and more about failing to regulate ourselves properly.

Impulsiveness can be defined as a process of action without conscious thought.

Breaking this down a bit further, impulsive behavior can be divided into three major categories: (1) motor, as in acting without thinking; (2) attention-related, which interferes with the ability to focus on the task at hand; and (3) faulty planning, which causes a person to focus almost exclusively on the present moment, with little thought given to future benefits, costs, or other considerations.

Some researchers believe that the chronic impulsivity displayed by adults with ADD can be traced to faulty "reward processing" in the brain. In laymen's terms, this means that for adults with ADD, the idea of delaying gratification on the way to a higher goal simply doesn't compute. While this can cause difficulties in childhood, it can really wreak havoc as a person moves through adulthood.

Despite the difficulties associated with a lifetime of impulsive habits, I believe it is possible to redirect behavior into more productive, positive, and deliberate actions. Being able to control impulses is one of the signs of a successful person. For adults with ADD, this fundamental lack of control makes the benefits of adulthood much harder to achieve—from getting a promotion, to finding a spouse, to being able to balance a checkbook.

In my opinion, the best way to overcome impulsivity is through meditation and mindfulness. These tools help a person gain a calmer, deeper, more thought-out approach to daily activities. Meditation has also been found to help adults with ADD reduce impulsive behavior.

Mindfulness is defined as a moment-by-moment awareness of thoughts, feelings, bodily sensations, and the surrounding environment. In practicing mindfulness, the goal is to be aware of any and all thoughts and sensations while trying not to judge or become actively involved in the thoughts. This is taught in many different forms and communities. One formal training, offered by therapists and backed by science, is called Mindfulness-Based Stress Reduction (MBSR). Once a person gets the hang of it, it can be practiced throughout the day. When MBSR is combined with some cognitive behavioral training, research shows it can decrease stress, impulsivity, and anxiety, among other symptoms.

Gaining a full understanding of mindfulness and meditation is beyond the scope of this book. However, I recommend two books on meditation that I find to be extremely helpful. The first is *Success through Stillness: Meditation Made Simple* by Russell Simmons. The second is *How to Meditate: A Practical Guide to*

Making Friends with Your Mind by Pema Chödrön, a famous female monk. Both books offer a practical guide to the art of meditation.

While my recommendation to introduce meditation and mindfulness into your daily life may sound good, I am aware that motivation is also a challenge for adults with ADD. To overcome this, I recommend "externalizing the motivation" by finding and joining a meditation center in your city. If you can't find a meditation group in your area, try the Insight Timer app. This app allows you to set a timer for your meditation and shows you other people around the world who are also meditating.

I did a silent, three-day meditation retreat. Being with others forced me to sit longer than I thought possible and gave me the confidence that I could meditate for at least twenty minutes a day. I now use the Insight Timer app and meditate once a day. I feel an amazing sense of calm after meditating—almost as if I'm defogging my brain. I carry this feeling with me throughout the day and week and reconnect to this sense of calm when I feel the urge to act impulsively.

In addition to learning meditation, I recommend these tips:

- Take the time to understand how the lack of impulse control associated with your ADD interferes in your daily life. Try to get a sense of the specific times, places, and circumstances that trigger an unwanted impulsive behavior. What negative outcomes does this behavior produce? Just the practice of being aware, even if after the fact, can help you build that muscle in your brain. For me, talking with customer-service representatives brings on impulsive anger. It's the sense that I am not understood that triggers me. Knowing this, I prepare for these interactions by calming myself down and asking if the call is necessary. If so, I do it when I'm relaxed and not in a rush. Being in control of my situation allows me to smile rather than become angry while on a call with the cable company.

- Make it harder to act impulsively. Try to put obstacles in the way of acting on your impulses. If you tend to go binge-shopping, for example, leave the credit card at home, or put an automatic hold on any purchase for twenty-four hours. I developed the bad habit of impulsively buying ice cream on my walk home from work. Instead of trying to control my impulsive need to eat something sweet, I changed the rules and the route home. The ice cream shop was out of sight and out of mind.

- If you tend to get in hot water for blurting out random thoughts during important work meetings, place a notebook nearby so you can write down your thoughts without disrupting the meeting at hand.

- Finally, engage in calming activities. Many times, the urge to act on impulse is the result of being overworked, stressed out, or on edge. This is especially true at the end of the day when cognitive resources are limited. Purposely adding relaxing activities to your routine can help take the edge off impulsive urges. It may be a matter of playing relaxing music or guided-imagery audio in the background at work. Some people enjoy taking walks or engaging in deep breathing exercises. You will know what works best for your particular situation.

You will have your own individual challenges and can develop work-around strategies with your behavioral therapist. These tips are an introduction to give you a sense of how bringing mindfulness and meditation into your life can help you get a handle on the impulsivity associated with ADD.

Daily Checklist

1. Set an alarm at 10:30 p.m. to wind down before bed.
2. Buy a water dispenser, and place it nearby.
3. Read *The Zone Diet* by Barry Sears to learn how to regulate glucose levels.
4. Find an exercise plan that is interesting, easy to start, and social.
5. Medication can work for focus and attention, but therapy or coaching is the best long-term solution.
6. Find a meditation center to learn how to meditate.

Daily Quiz

What is the best way to overcome impulsivity?

a) Learn to meditate.
b) Eat McDonalds daily.
c) Binge on Netflix.

Correct Answer: a

DAY 9
Impulsive Communication

*I'm such a blabbermouth. I always say
things I shouldn't and then get in so much
trouble. My friends stopped confiding in
me. Is there a way I can stop this?*
—JACK, HARTFORD

Having Adult ADD makes the above scenario all too common. We say and do things impulsively. For me, I find that there are three areas where my impulsive communication gets me in trouble.

The first is impulsively agreeing to things that I don't want to do.

The second is gossiping. I have come to see that both are born out of low self-esteem and a need to please others.

The third is impulsively sending e-mails that I later regret. They're often angry missives that diminish my power and make me look immature.

Becoming aware of my particular impulsive communication issues has helped me control my speech and communication. I now rarely say yes to things I don't want to do. Occasionally, however, I find myself reverting to old, impulsive patterns, gossiping and sending regrettable e-mails.

If these situations strike a chord with you—don't worry. Change is possible.

In my practice, I find that most adults with ADD fall prey to two common faux pas when it comes to communicating with the rest of the world: (1) saying things they regret, and (2) sending things they regret (via e-mail, text message, phone, or social media).

Truth told, the second challenge is easier to solve, so let's explore some strategies on that first. With regard to impulsive texting, I recommend adding software to your phone. I downloaded GO SMS Pro for my Android phone. This software gives me a few seconds after sending a text to stop it, thereby preventing impulsive messages. Another similar app for both the Android and the iPhone is On Second Thought.

For e-mails, Gmail has a function that allows you to set a period of time during which you can quickly undo a sent e-mail. To turn on the "Undo Send" feature on your computer, open Gmail. In the top right, click "Settings." In the "Undo Send" section, check the box next to "Enable Undo Send." In the "Send Cancellation Period" section, set the amount of time you want to before sending an e-mail.

The next time you send an impulsive e-mail, look for the word "Undo" at the top of the e-mail. Quickly click this button, and you can stop the impulsive e-mail from being sent. The challenge here is to make sure you watch for that button every time you send a message. For Outlook, you have to change the rules settings. Search "change rules setting in Outlook" for more information on that feature.

With regard to phone conversations, I like the approach adopted by one of my clients. He is in sales, a field in which phone skills can mean the difference between success and failure. His approach is to put his phone on mute when his clients are talking. This prevents him from jumping in with an impulsive comment that interrupts his sales prospect. To speak, he has to take the added step of unmuting the phone. This process forces him to slow down so he can guide his communication in a more professional and powerful direction. I love this idea.

Controlling face-to-face conversations, on the other hand, requires much more intensive intervention. First of all, other than clamping your hands over your mouth, there's no way to automatically press "mute" when you're speaking in person. A few common pitfalls include:

- Interrupting
- Talking too much
- Talking too fast
- Going off track
- Not paying attention
- Not maintaining conversational balance
- Impulsively blurting out words or comments that would be better left unsaid
- Failing to read facial cues or body language

One of the first things I recommend for my clients with Adult ADD is to take stock of the kinds of situations in which impulsive communication is particularly troublesome. For example, do you find yourself most prone to gaffes when you are anxious to please others? Is it when you are trying to prove your value? If people pleasing is your weakness, try to preempt failure by going into situations with greater awareness and self-control. Try mapping out the conversation—either in your mind or even on paper—before you step foot in the room.

Some people have trouble at cocktail parties. The combination of sensory overload from the sights, sounds, and people in the room, along with a bit of alcohol, can quickly send most adults with ADD into a tailspin. Here too, think about a strategy that will help you reign in your verbal impulsivity. Perhaps it's best to force yourself not to speak until you have circled the room (at a normal pace) a couple of times, so you can get used to your surroundings. Or maybe it's a matter of offering to get the drinks or hors d'oeuvres for your friends first—without talking—before joining the general conversation. Whatever strategy you pick, envision yourself succeeding before the party.

My biggest challenges always occurred during office or business meetings. Luckily, my mother gave me a good piece of advice that I am happy to pass on to you. She once said, "Always be the last to speak at the meeting. It makes you seem more powerful." Instituting this one simple rule helps me keep my impulsivity in check and allows me to gather important information before speaking. It also increases the perception that I am patient, interested in what others have to say, and able to manage my impulses. These are all signs of personal power, which translates well in the halls of corporate America.

Beyond these particular situations, there are some general rules, strategies, and habits that adults with ADD can cultivate to improve their overall verbal interactions with other people. The following is a brief review.

- First, knowledge is power. Ask friends and family for feedback on your conversational weaknesses.
- Next, set reasonable goals. If you have difficulty in person, at the office, and at parties after work, don't try to correct everything at once. Pick one area in which you think you can develop better conversational skills. Master these situations before you move on to the next. As the old saying goes, success breeds success.
- Finally, create a system of prompts to help you stay focused during certain social situations. These may include setting your phone or watch to vibrate every few minutes to remind you to adopt a slower, quieter tone.

By nature, humans are verbal creatures. Words, and especially face-to-face conversations, are the key to human connection. Having ADD can be a serious impediment to this basic building block of social interaction. Nevertheless, taking steps to develop a more thoughtful approach to your speech will send a message that you are winning the battle for self-control.

Daily Checklist

1. Set an alarm at 10:30 p.m. to wind down before bed.
2. Buy a water dispenser, and place it nearby.
3. Read *The Zone Diet* by Barry Sears to learn how to regulate glucose levels.
4. Find an exercise plan that is interesting, easy to start, and social.
5. Medication can work for focus and attention, but therapy or coaching is the best long-term solution.
6. Find a meditation center to learn how to meditate.
7. Download the On Second Thought app, and use the "Undo Send" feature in e-mail.

Daily Quiz

What is best way to manage impulsive texting?

a) Download Go SMS Pro or On Second Thought software.
b) Text while driving. This will certainly slow you down from impulsive behavior.
c) Text after having five drinks. It will calm you down.

Correct Answer: a

DAY 10
Unhelpful Emotions

*I seem to get angry so quickly. I totally
flipped out at the bank when the teller took
a phone call on her cell. Is this normal?*
—JANE, OREGON

ngry much? Probably, if you have Adult ADD. Emotional dysregulation is one of the main hallmark symptoms of Adult ADD. If you have Adult ADD, you have less control over your emotions. We get sadder, angrier, and are more excitable than the average person.

Why is this?

The frontal lobe, or the "adult" part of our brain that allows us to think before acting, can't communicate effectively with the primitive, "childlike" part of our brain, the amygdala. When you feel a tantrum come on, the frontal lobe isn't able to gain control over this childlike part of the brain, leading to a total meltdown of emotions. And medication isn't a magic pill.

I myself struggle with preventing my meltdowns, particularly when talking with customer service representatives on the phone. Most people struggle with these calls, but "losing it" takes on new meaning if you have Adult ADD.

What can we do to manage our anger?

The first step is to "box it up." Angry feelings can come on so quickly that you need a response that is already practiced and available—a quick-response strategy that acts when your brain can't.

When you get angry, imagine a box around you, protecting you from those in your vicinity. This box is your safe zone. Mine has a sign on it that reads, "Danger...Do Not Cross."

Once you visualize the box around you, expel all the air from your lungs. Don't breathe in—breathe out. Get all the air out of your lungs. The body will take care of the rest, naturally refilling your lungs and creating an autonomic response of relaxation.

Do this three times: Expel all the air from your lungs, and let them refill naturally. Finally, walk away from what is provoking your anger. Science shows that once the anger system is activated, all rational thought is impossible. Take an hour to settle down and come back with a more clear and level head.

Another method for managing anger is to recognize your triggers and simply avoid those scenarios. If you can't avoid the situation, then delegate the task to another. Maybe you lose it like me when on the phone with a customer service rep. If that's true, then have your partner make these calls, and you can offer to do the dishes instead.

Managing anger if you have Adult ADD is not easy, but these tips can be a helpful addition to your toolbox. Anger is not the only impulsive emotion adults with ADD struggle with every day. Has anyone ever called you a drama queen or an adrenaline junkie? Impulsively seeking excitement can lead to a road of ruin.

In many adults with ADD, the reward centers of the brain do not fire properly. This leads to feelings of understimulation and a desire for excitement and sensation seeking, which is why adults with ADD often have problems with gambling, drugs, sex, and overeating. Seeking excitement in one's life is not bad. I myself have enjoyed skydiving from fifteen thousand feet and scuba diving in a cavern. But both activities were done with an instructor in a safe manner. The problem arises when an adult with ADD manufacturers excitement at the wrong times with the wrong people for the wrong reasons.

We call this "drama."

For some adults with ADD, this "drama," or "negative excitement," serves the immediate purpose of stimulating the reward centers of the brain. The costs of this behavior, however, can be detrimental to oneself and loved ones. Reducing self-created "drama" takes time and is best accomplished with a therapist to help you stop your triggers and develop new coping mechanisms for unhealthy acting-out behaviors.

The most important element to changing this behavior is to recognize negative excitement-seeking as a symptom of Adult ADD and to recognize that it may not be born out of some childhood issue. Learning that the Adult ADD brain craves excitement or rewards is helpful to creating change. Start slow, and check in with yourself about what you need to feel complete.

Is it a huge manufactured fight with your partner, a chocolate cake at 3:00 a.m., or a vacation to a new and exciting place that brings fun, spontaneity, and passion to your life?

I pick number three.

Daily Checklist:

1. Set an alarm at 10:30 p.m. to wind down before bed.
2. Buy a water dispenser, and place it nearby.
3. Read *The Zone Diet* by Barry Sears to learn how to regulate glucose levels.
4. Find an exercise plan that is interesting, easy to start, and social.
5. Medication can work for focus and attention, but therapy or coaching is the best long-term solution.
6. Find a meditation center to learn how to meditate.
7. Download the On Second Thought app, and use the "Undo Send" feature in e-mail.
8. When angry, imagine a box around you, and exhale all the air in your lungs.

Daily Quiz

What is best way to manage anger?

a) Avoid your triggers.
b) Breathe out all the air in your lungs. The rest will take care of itself.
c) Imagine yourself in a box that protects you.

Correct Answer: a, b, and c

DAY 11
Toxic Shame

*I get really down on myself and can't
seem to shake my self-doubt. I'm afraid
to try anything new because I'll just screw
it up. How do I get out of this funk?*
—HENRY P.

Just as it is difficult to self-regulate anger with Adult ADD, it can be equally hard to manage the negative feelings. Adults with ADD are prone to more sadness and depressive feelings than adults without ADD. Our highs are higher, and our lows are lower. The feelings we experience can be more intense and harder to control.

One of the emotional problems associated with Adult ADD is toxic shame. In fact, toxic shame should be listed as one of the core symptoms of Adult ADD, in addition to impulsivity, inattention, and disorganization. If you are like me, you were diagnosed later in life, and years of frustration, spills, mishaps, mistakes, screwups, and the f-word (failure) accumulated throughout your life. This feeling of chronic failure often leads to toxic shame.

Healthy shame stops us from burping in an elevator or taking a seat on a bus when a pregnant woman is standing nearby. Toxic shame, however, is felt on a deeper level and for longer periods of time. It causes us to isolate and feel such self-loathing that depression may follow.

What happens to a person who spends a lifetime struggling with toxic shame?

Years of failure lead to fear of failure, which breeds avoidance. We have a history of not achieving our potential, and we decide to avoid failure by not trying. This act of distorted self-love preserves our self-esteem. But it also keeps us small and stuck. A fear-based attitude limits our potential. What is the one thing that you always wanted to do but didn't feel you could? Write a novel? Start a company? Get married? The key to overcoming your fear of toxic shame and fear of failure is through support. This takes work, but it can be accomplished.

Here are three ways to manage toxic shame and fear of failure:

The first step is realizing it's not you—it's your ADD. As the famous song says, "Blame it on the ADD." This helps to diminish the global feeling of failure and worthlessness. You may struggle in some areas, but you have unique gifts in others.

The next step is not to isolate yourself and hide when the toxic shame takes over. This is a very hard thing to do, but it's the only way to beat back the horrible feelings that one is not worthy. If you stay engaged with others, you will slowly realize that the shame is all in your head. Others simply don't care that much about your mistakes. If they do, they certainly will lose interest in them sooner than you will.

By not hiding, you will realize that your self-loathing and shame is not shared by others. They like you and want the best for you. Over time, you will realize that the only person who thinks that you're a total failure is *you!*

If being with the people you know is hard, try people who you don't know. Join a mastermind group. Mastermind groups are great ways to get the support you need to move past your shame and fears.

What is a mastermind group? Mastermind groups offer a combination of brainstorming, peer accountability and support in a group setting. A mastermind group helps you and your mastermind group members develop your ideas in a safe supportive environment and achieve success. You can also start your own mastermind group. Don't let fear of failure hold you back. Be the master of your mind. Walk through the fear and avoidance with the help of a supportive group.

When toxic shame takes over, externalize the problem. "Blame it on the ADD," recognizing that your Adult ADD is at work. You have many wonderful gifts to offer the world. Instead of hiding, find a friend or group to be with. Stay present with those around you. Don't run away. Find a support system that believes in you. This may be people who don't know you and don't judge you as harshly as you judge yourself.

Daily Checklist

1. Set an alarm at 10:30 p.m. to wind down before bed.
2. Buy a water dispenser, and place it nearby.
3. Read *The Zone Diet* by Barry Sears to learn how to regulate glucose levels.
4. Find an exercise plan that is interesting, easy to start, and social.
5. Medication can work for focus and attention, but therapy or coaching is the best long-term solution.
6. Find a meditation center to learn how to meditate.
7. Download the On Second Thought app, and use the "Undo Send" feature in e-mail.
8. When angry, imagine a box around you, and exhale all the air in your lungs.
9. Join a mastermind group to avoid toxic shame and fear of failure.

Daily Quiz

What is best way to manage toxic shame and fear of failure?

a) Find a mastermind group or similar supportive group to help you with your goals.
b) Avoid all social interactions for one year.
c) Crawl into bed, and pull the covers over your head.

Correct Answer: a

DAY 12
Compassion and Community

We are embarking on a journey together. On this path, you will experience many feelings, such as frustration, anger, shame, boredom, excitement, and self-doubt. But, to be successful, we also need compassion for ourselves.

If you have Adult ADD, you've probably heard the phrase, "Don't be so hard on yourself." What does this mean? Whenever I heard this, I was stumped as to what the person was referring to. I thought, "I should be even harder on myself. Maybe then I wouldn't make so many mistakes!" I would continue doing what I was doing, but with even more intensity. Of course, this was the wrong approach, and it led to more failure and pain.

It was only when I learned about Adult ADD that I was able to see that I wasn't "the mistake." It was the choices I was making that were the problem. The key was to assess what was working and what was not, to use my strengths, and to avoid tasks or jobs that highlighted my weaknesses. With that awareness, I could develop compassion for myself.

For instance, being an administrative assistant was not going to work for me. After finding a career that called upon my strengths, I started having more success. From that place, when I made a mistake, I wasn't as hard on myself. I knew what I was good at and what I wasn't good at. When I had an ADD screwup, I told myself that it was not me. It was simply my ADD. I had enough belief in my strengths to allow me not to get too down on myself for the mistakes.

In short, the next time you hear someone say, "Don't be so hard on yourself," realize that they are really saying, "Focus on your strengths. You have many!"

Reading this book, and taking the accompanying course, is a wonderful way to start managing and overcoming your Adult ADD. But a huge part of my success—and my ability to make peace with my own ADD—has to do with my commitment to personal growth.

What does this mean?

I define personal growth as a desire to learn more about ourselves, our relationships, and how we show up in the world. A lot can be learned from books (and I've recommended a few in this thirty-day course).

I also believe that the best way to grow as a person is through a personal and spiritual-growth community. This can be a church, synagogue, mosque, sports team, club, ashram, meditation center or mastermind group. The location and the community can be determined by you. To really grow as a person, a number of important factors must be present to learn about yourself.

The most important factor is having a sense of safety and a feeling that you are cared for and loved. Love might be a strong word here, but it is important that those around you are also motivated to see you grow.

A second factor is the culture of feedback. Do you get regular feedback, provided in a caring manner? How can we grow if we do not receive feedback on our progress? The feedback can be informal or formal, but there should be a culture of feedback that is healthy.

The third and final factor is that there are levels to grow into, and that you feel a bit scared rising to each new level. Without that sense of stretching (and the accompanying fear), growth may not occur. This also can be formal, with actual levels and ranks or certifications, or informal via supportive conversations.

My personal growth has occurred within many different communities. I am a member of a formal personal-growth community called the ManKind Project (mankindproject.org), which supports men in developing their emotional maturity. I have been a member, along with my brother and father, for thirteen years and have risen in the ranks thanks to mentorship and feedback.

I also recently joined another community called Momentum Education. This community focuses on goal setting and helping members step into fear to achieve their goals. Feedback is a huge part of this community and is offered every step of the way.

I've also benefited from individual therapy and a training program in Gestalt therapy that meets every summer for a two-week residential experience. Feedback is built into those two weeks, and my psychotherapy skills are critiqued in a supportive manner.

Scuba diving with the Professional Association of Diving Instructors (PADI) is also something I've stretched into and have grown tremendously from. It used to be a phobia of mine to be under water at those depths, but through practice, coaching, and guidance, I have overcome my fears. Last winter I actually dove in an underground cavern in Mexico. It was a thrilling personal growth challenge and opportunity.

I encourage you to find a community that supports your personal growth. If you're in one already, you are on your way to becoming the butterfly you were always meant to be.

Daily Checklist

1. Set an alarm at 10:30 p.m. to wind down before bed.
2. Buy a water dispenser, and place it nearby.
3. Read *The Zone Diet* by Barry Sears to learn how to regulate glucose levels.
4. Find an exercise plan that is interesting, easy to start, and social.
5. Medication can work for focus and attention, but therapy or coaching is the best long-term solution.
6. Find a meditation center to learn how to meditate.
7. Download the On Second Thought app, and use the "Undo Send" feature in e-mail.
8. When angry, imagine a box around you, and exhale all the air in your lungs.
9. Join a mastermind group to avoid toxic shame and fear of failure.
10. Find a personal and spiritual-growth community that offers you helpful feedback and caring support.

Daily Quiz

What is the most important quality in any personal and spiritual-growth community?

a) Low membership fee
b) Love
c) Good cookies and coffee

Correct Answer: b

Day 13 & 14: Weekend Review

Self-Regulation and Impulsivity

Learn to meditate as a way to become more mindful and conscious of your impulsive behaviors. Join a local meditation center to get the basics and confidence to meditate alone. Download the Insight Timer app to meditate at home.

Impulsive Communication

Develop strategies to control your impulsive verbal and written communication. Talk last in meetings. Download the On Second Thought app, and use the "Undo Send" feature for e-mails.

Unhealthy Emotions

If angry, imagine a safe box around yourself and exhale all the air from your lungs. Learn your triggers for impulsive anger and rage. Avoid or delegate tasks that make you angry easily. Choose to sidestep drama in favor of healthy hobbies or activities that bring you excitement.

Toxic Shame

Overcome toxic shame by finding a supportive community of people who don't judge you as harshly as you judge yourself. Stay connected. Mastermind groups are great ways to get support with personal and business goals.

Compassion and Community

Find a supportive personal- or spiritual-growth community that comes to love you, supports you, and offers you helpful feedback.

DAY 15
Reputation Management

I always get overlooked for promotions. Is there
something I'm doing that sends the wrong signals?
—TIM, NEW YORK

s your desk always messy? Are your clothes wrinkled? Is your handbag stuffed with junk? Are you always late? If you have Adult ADD, your actions speak louder than words, and your reputation may have suffered.

It's harsh, but your bosses, coworkers, and even loved ones may not respect you. They won't always tell you this directly, but through their actions, you may feel that you're not as valued as others.

I help my Adult ADD clients see that their exterior presentation and actions are as important as their interior mindset. It's important to understand that we all have a reputation that is worth managing carefully.

I call this "Reputation Management." Reputation management is about becoming conscious of the impact that our appearances and actions have on others.

In my twenties and thirties, my reputation needed significant improvement. I was clueless, however, as to how others saw me. Coworkers would get promoted over me, and I couldn't figure out why. Looking back, it was very simple. Due to my ADD symptoms, I appeared disorganized, chaotic, and disheveled. I wasn't accountable, and my reputation suffered.

What does it mean to be accountable? In simple terms, accountability means that you do what you say you're going to do. People who are accountable follow through with their words and make commitments that they keep. They don't blame others for their faults. They accept responsibility for their actions. People who are accountable are trusted.

Follow-through is a significant problem for people with Adult ADD. Flaking on others breeds distrust, which leads to distancing, loneliness, and isolation for the adult with ADD. This creates an unhealthy cycle of people pleasing and overcommitment to prove your worth. The cycle becomes hard to maintain, leading to more broken promises, poor follow-through, lack of accountability, and greater distrust!

It's a vicious cycle.

For many years, I was not accountable and didn't understand why others wouldn't trust me, hire me or promote me. It was only when I joined a men's support group (mankindproject.org) where others held me accountable that I learned the value of being a man of my word.

That was fifteen years ago. Now I can hold others accountable.

Being accountable is a high-level skill for those with Adult ADD and can truly only be attained when the other more basic skills of self-care, time management, and organization are mastered. These skills will be discussed in subsequent lessons.

Until mastery occurs, it's really best to undercommit, underpromise, and manage expectations—particularly for larger projects or tasks. Maybe you should decline to be your friend's maid of honor if committing would require a great deal of planning. Saying no or declining offers will help rebuild trust as you can't fail to follow through on something you didn't agree to do. Your friend might be temporarily disappointed, but if you explain the reasons, she will certainly understand. We will cover more of this in a future lesson.

At the same time, you can improve your reputation by delivering on small acts of accountability. Offer to take out the garbage or wash the dishes and actually follow through. Notice the impact your small acts of accountability have on your relationships.

Of course, if you have a job where you're expected to follow through on big projects, it's important to manage expectations. Often those with ADD overcompensate for past failures by offering unrealistic deadlines, trying to show how productive and efficient they can be. When they fail to meet these unrealistic deadlines, they fall back into the black hole of self-loathing and self-doubt.

Manage your boss's or partner's expectations by adding more time to deadlines. Believe me, *you will need it*. If you don't have a deadline, set one, and give yourself more time than you think that you'll need. Realistic deadlines provide external motivation for reaching your goals.

I have a very bright client who works in software development. His boss has grown increasingly frustrated with him. The reason he's annoyed with my client is not that my client doesn't finish projects on time. Rather, it's because he doesn't communicate that he needs more time and assistance. If he would only communicate more, managing his boss's expectations, his job would not be in jeopardy. Accountability is not just about getting things done. It's also about managing expectations and, when necessary, clearly renegotiating deadlines.

Be a man or woman of your word. Manage your reputation. Start with small achievable promises. Say no to larger tasks where success is less guaranteed. Manage expectations. Renegotiate deadlines or commitments.

Be accountable, and reap the fruits of trust and connection.

Daily Checklist

1. Set an alarm at 10:30 p.m. to wind down before bed.
2. Buy a water dispenser, and place it nearby.
3. Read *The Zone Diet* by Barry Sears to learn how to regulate glucose levels.
4. Find an exercise plan that is interesting, easy to start, and social.
5. Medication can work for focus and attention, but therapy or coaching is the best long-term solution.
6. Find a meditation center to learn how to meditate.
7. Download the On Second Thought app, and use the "Undo Send" feature in e-mail.
8. When angry, imagine a box around you, and exhale all the air in your lungs.
9. Join a mastermind group to avoid toxic shame and fear of failure.
10. Find a personal and spiritual-growth community that offers you helpful feedback and caring support.
11. Politely decline large projects or tasks where success is not guaranteed. Follow through on small ones to build trust.

Daily Quiz

What is the best way to manage your reputation?

a) Follow through on promises.
b) Be on time.
c) Have a clean desk.

Correct answer: a, b, and c

Time Management

I can't seem to get anywhere on time. I'm always
fifteen minutes late, and my husband is so
angry with me. He thinks I don't care about him.
But I do! I can't seem to get my act together.
—KERRY O., NEW YORK

Are you always late? Do you find yourself constantly disappointing your friends, family and coworkers for not showing up on time for key appointments? Do you ignore the clock when you have to leave the house because you have "just one more thing to take care of?" Do you sincerely wish you could learn to be on time, but secretly fear that chronic lateness is just a part of who you are?

Time management is relationship management!

If my description strikes a familiar chord with you, I'd like to let you in on a little secret: I've been there, done that, and bought the T-shirt. As someone who has struggled with Adult ADD, I vividly recall the days when I simply could not show up anywhere on time. I also remember the frustration and disappointment on the faces of the people I kept letting down. Their reactions to my chronic lateness usually depended on how long they had known me, but the pattern was always the same. The first few times I was late, people were willing to cut me some slack. After a while, my inability to show up on time became a major issue in my relationships. Girlfriends gave warnings. Bosses issued ultimatums. Parents and relatives stopped even trying. Slowly but surely I watched as a "quirk" in my personality morphed into a permanent label. I was branded with the scarlet "L" of lateness.

It was not until I joined a men's support group, in which an honest exchange of thoughts and feelings was valued, that I truly began to understand that my lateness hurt other people. I remember very clearly an older man firmly chastising me for being late, outlining the impact of my "choice" to not arrive on time. The consequence of my relentless tardiness was that I would lose respect from others and that they may not trust me. I was also filled with a sense of shame each time I was late. This shame was unconscious at the time, but with awareness, I realized that I was perpetuating my toxic shame every time I was late. It became clear that chronic lateness—and the associated failures in relationships and life—was slowly destroying my self-esteem.

This man gave me a gift by holding me accountable, which led to a fundamental shift in my thinking. I was able to see that time management is relationship management. If I wanted relationships, I needed to be accountable and on time. This realization was huge for me. In the past, I would rush out of the house to meet a time goal. For example, if I had a 10:00 a.m.

appointment, I would focus on the time as a goal. Now I see the connection with whomever I'm meeting as the real goal, and the stakes of being late are much higher.

This man also asked me, hypothetically, if I would still be late if a million dollars was given to the people who arrived on time to the meeting. I replied honesty and answered no. I would be there an hour early. It became clear that I could be on time if the stakes were high enough. I also realized that I was not valuing others' needs as equally as my own needs. I was being selfish and hiding under the label of my Adult ADD.

This idea of being on time also reflects the theme of "reputation management" discussed in an earlier lesson. It's very simple. If I'm early or on time to appointments, others will trust me, and my reputation will soar. Once I realized that my lateness negatively impacted someone's ability to trust me (or promote me at work), it was easier to accept that I had to change.

Awareness of the impact of my lateness on others was the first step for me to change. The next step was to fully experience the wonderful feeling of being on time. I began to check in with my feelings on the occasions when I did show up on time. I noticed that being punctual helped me feel better about myself and relieved the shame I was carrying around. As I sat there, early for an appointment, I noticed the pride and joy I felt in being punctual—and that it was someone else showing up late for a change. Connecting to that pleasurable feeling of being on time was critical. I wanted to feel that again and again, thus further fueling the motivation to be on time.

Over the next few years, I gained mastery of time management and could begin to hold others accountable for being late.

Being aware of the impact of lateness on others, and on your-self, is the most important factor in learning to be on time.

There are other tools and tricks that I employ to be on time consistently. But before we focus on what you can do to show up on time, it is important to clear up misconceptions about how adults with ADD relate to time in general. You may unknowingly harbor these misconceptions yourself, so it's vital that you gain an understanding of some basic concepts if you want to move on to the next step.

Contrary to what many people assume, the vast majority of adults with ADD do not intend to be inconsiderate or disre-spectful when they show up late for an appointment. Instead, it all goes back to how your brain is wired. Research shows that the Adult ADD brain is wired for stimulation. To anyone with ADD, this is probably not news. What is news is that how your brain is wired has a direct impact on how you relate to time. Adults without ADD operate within the familiar time frames of past, present, and future. Adults with ADD, on the other hand, view the world in just two time frames: now and not now.

"Now" is whatever is in front of you at the moment. The meeting that's supposed to take place in twenty minutes? That's called "not now." To make matters more complicated, to the ADD mind, now always takes precedence over not now. What does this look like in everyday life? Consider the following now/not now problems:

- The manager who delays writing his meeting agenda until moments before the staff meeting, because he's focused on cleaning crumbs from his keyboard.

- The hostess who does not start cooking until minutes before the dinner party. She's more worried about what she will wear to the event.
- The dad who keeps surfing the Internet instead of cooking dinner for his family.

Left to their own devices, adults with ADD do not see these actions as rude, insensitive, or careless. Rudeness has to be intentional to count. For someone living in a binary now/not now world, the impact on others of being late does not factor into the rudeness equation. Nevertheless, to the rest of the world, it's not much of an excuse. It may not be intentional rudeness, but it is still felt as rudeness by friends, family, and coworkers. Furthermore, because the rest of the world views time as late or not late, failing to modify this core way of behaving inevitably wreaks havoc on relationships.

Being on time requires answering another key question: "What must I stop doing to be on time?" Adults with ADD suffer from "One-More-Thing-Itis." This occurs when you're trying to get somewhere on time but decide to do one more thing before going out the door. Often that one more thing is completely unnecessary and not essential to your appointment. Examples of these I've heard from clients include:

- Deciding to organize your closet ten minutes before leaving the house.
- Changing the batteries in all the smoke detectors instead of getting your papers together for a big meeting.
- And the biggest time suck of them all: checking your e-mail.

I recommend saying no to yourself out loud. It is well known that the internal voice of reason is weak in adults with ADD. To counteract this, speak out loud and say no the next time you find yourself doing one more thing before you leave the house.

Being on time comes down to saying no to yourself and yes to the people in your life.

Speaking of getting out of the door, many adults with ADD find the simple task of walking out the door nearly impossible to do in one fell swoop. Keys go missing, important folders disappear, phones get left under the bed. This can lead to a lot of extraneous running around—and wasted time—prior to leaving the house. The remedy for avoiding last minute distractions is to prepare beforehand. It may seem childish to lay out your supplies the night before, but it works. Leave a large note on the door that reminds you to make sure you have everything you need—an itemized, specific list: keys, directions, phone, important papers, wallet, money, snack. Incorporating this step into your routine will help you master the fine art of showing up on time. You will be amazed by how much stress can be relieved by this one fix.

If you still have challenges showing up on time, ask loved ones about the impact of your choice to put your needs first and theirs second. Ask for fearless feedback. Tough love is still loving.

Daily Checklist

1. Set an alarm at 10:30 p.m. to wind down before bed.
2. Buy a water dispenser, and place it nearby.
3. Read *The Zone Diet* by Barry Sears to learn how to regulate glucose levels.
4. Find an exercise plan that is interesting, easy to start, and social.
5. Medication can work for focus and attention, but therapy or coaching is the best long-term solution.
6. Find a meditation center to learn how to meditate.
7. Download the On Second Thought app, and use the "Undo Send" feature in e-mail.
8. When angry, imagine a box around you, and exhale all the air in your lungs.
9. Join a mastermind group to avoid toxic shame and fear of failure.
10. Find a personal and spiritual-growth community that offers you helpful feedback and caring support.
11. Politely decline large projects or tasks where success is not guaranteed. Follow through on small ones to build trust.
12. Say "No" out loud to yourself when you find yourself doing "one more thing."

Daily Quiz

What is best way to stop One-More-Thing-Itis?

a) Stop and say no to yourself out loud when you begin to do one more thing.
b) Take an aspirin and a nap.
c) Call the chiropractor.

Correct Answer: a

DAY 17
Overcommitment

B eyond the issue of chronic lateness, overcommitment is the second half of the one-two punch that knocks out adults with ADD. As with many symptoms associated with ADD, the urge to promise much (and, unfortunately, deliver little) does not necessarily come from rudeness or a lack of consideration for other people's feelings. Often, it's just the opposite. Many people with ADD are "people pleasers" who overcommit to projects that they can't possibly complete. The result is a lack of accountability and a poor reputation.

Where does this propensity to overcommit come from? Sometimes it's a reaction to years of disappointing friends and family. Our insecure fear that we are seen as failures pushes us to want to please others and receive the validation we so desperately want. In my case, I had developed a reputation of letting people down. Even if my actions were unintentional and due to my ADD symptoms, I thought that the best way to repair the damage would be to make promises and deliver on them. Each time someone asked me for a favor or to take on a project, I said yes, hoping to show the world, once and for all, that I could make good on my word. Unfortunately, instead of helping to repair my reputation, piling on obligations turned out to be a recipe for disaster.

Thankfully, I have learned to manage the challenges of over-committing. Over the years, I realized it is possible to say no without feeling guilty. I've also learned that it is possible to say yes without messing up.

As mentioned, the mistake of overcommitting usually comes from a need for acceptance, which is rooted in a lifetime of rejection and criticism. Unfortunately, once the promise has been made, the ADD mind shifts into gear. We misjudge the amount of time tasks should take, or we procrastinate and allow ourselves to get distracted.

One client recently told me about a very typical experience. He offered to fix an elderly neighbor's front door. His goal was to save her the time and expense of finding a contractor for such a "small" job. After all, how long could it take? Just a few minutes, right? All he needed to do was run to the hardware store and grab a couple of things.

Four weeks later, my client still had not completed the project. Instead of basking in the praise of a good deed done, he found himself avoiding his neighbor, ignoring her calls, and once again demonstrating his incompetence to yet another person.

So what can an adult with ADD do to end the habit of overcommitting?

The first step is to master what I like to call the Warren Buffet rule. Mr. Buffet is fond of saying that the difference between successful people and really successful people is that really successful people say no to almost everything. Think about that statement for a moment: you can improve productivity by reducing activity. If one of the wealthiest and most successful businessmen on the planet can say no, then so can you. Warren Buffet helps a lot of people in his life—yet he gives himself permission to say no most of the time. The judicious use of the word no allows him to say yes only when doing so is likely to bring the best results.

How can you implement your own Buffet rule? I have found that having an actual script of what to say is very helpful. Since adults with ADD live in the present, we generally don't think about what we will say in a hypothetical situation. We live in the moment, and we answer in the moment. As such, when someone asks us a question, we tend to answer with whatever enters into our mind at the time. Usually the answer to a request for a favor is yes, which is what gets us into trouble.

When asked to take something on, ask yourself, "What would Warren Buffet do?" He would likely have a script of polite refusals ready on the tip of his tongue. The following phrases can help you keep yourself from committing to something you cannot deliver on without losing a friend in the process.

Start each of these phrases with, "I would love to help, but...

- I'm in the middle of several projects.
- I'm not taking on any new responsibilities just now.
- My calendar is full at the moment.
- I have no experience with that.
- I have another commitment that is taking up my time.

If, for some reason, you are uncomfortable saying a polite no at the moment of the request, you can still put the brakes on the commitment by simply saying, "Let me check my calendar and get back to you." These phrases keep you from getting yourself into hot water by making an instant decision that you will later regret.

In addition to having a ready response, reining in the impulse to overcommit also requires a concerted effort to slow down your thinking. In this context, slowing down your thinking means becoming more aware of the process that goes into the way you make decisions.

First, take some time to prioritize the relationships in your life. Obviously saying yes to your spouse, boss, or children should take precedence over the neighbor you hardly know, or even your friends. Get in the habit of drawing a mental circle around the most important people in your life, and then make a commitment not to get involved in other people's requests.

Second, realize that just because someone asks you to do something does not mean you are the only person capable of fulfilling that request. Yes, it's flattering to be asked to help someone out. But remember, in most cases, the person asking for the favor has a whole network of people to ask. Allow yourself to understand that people not in your immediate circle of need, in almost all cases, do not need you. They need someone to do a favor for them—and you happen to be in front of them at the moment. That's a completely different concept than "needing" your help.

Third, manage your own expectations in terms of what you can get done in a day. As an adult with ADD, you probably like to think that every day holds endless possibilities. The truth, as you know, is much different. Be realistic about what you can accomplish and then cut that in half and commit to that!

In addition to slowing your thinking and setting boundaries around relationships and time, adults with ADD can also avoid overcommitting by setting boundaries around their self-esteem. Focus on your opinion of yourself at the time you agree to help someone out. Do you often say yes because you actually want to help, or are you afraid to say no? This fear can come in several forms. You may fear making the other person angry. You might fear losing their love or respect. Or you may fear feeling disappointed by the fact that you are actually human, with limited time, just like everyone else.

Rejecting the urge to be perfect is another "self-boundary" that can help adults with ADD keep their commitments under control. In business, there is a saying, "Perfect is the enemy of good enough." In the real world, good enough is often what it takes to get things done. When you decide to take on a project, get in the habit of asking yourself, "Is what I've done good enough for now?"

Learning to limit the number of commitments you make takes time and practice. There will be times when you forget to set up your boundaries and find yourself feeling as if you are right back where you started. This is normal and natural. If you see yourself falling back into the old habits of taking on tasks to please people or to prove you are competent, remember to take a step back and review the tips we've discussed.

Daily Checklist

1. Set an alarm at 10:30 p.m. to wind down before bed.
2. Buy a water dispenser, and place it nearby.
3. Read *The Zone Diet* by Barry Sears to learn how to regulate glucose levels.
4. Find an exercise plan that is interesting, easy to start, and social.
5. Medication can work for focus and attention, but therapy or coaching is the best long-term solution.
6. Find a meditation center to learn how to meditate.
7. Download the On Second Thought app, and use the "Undo Send" feature in e-mail.
8. When angry, imagine a box around you, and exhale all the air in your lungs.
9. Join a mastermind group to avoid toxic shame and fear of failure.
10. Find a personal and spiritual-growth community that offers you helpful feedback and caring support.
11. Politely decline large projects or tasks where success is not guaranteed. Follow through on small ones to build trust.
12. Say "No" out loud to yourself when you find yourself doing "one more thing."
13. Have a phrase ready ("I would love to, but...") to use when someone asks you to do something.

Daily Quiz

What is an effective way to handle overcommitment?

a) Have a phrase ready to say when someone asks you to do something. Example: "I'd love to, but my calendar is full."
b) Say yes to everything. People will like you then.
c) Practice saying no. Others will respect you for your honesty.

Correct Answer: a and c

DAY 18
Productivity

I feel like some days I'm spinning in circles,
or totally stuck in the mud. I can't get things
done and my boss is getting pissed with me.
—JENNIFER P., NEW JERSEY

et's face it. Whether a person has ADD or not, the modern office can be a place of constant distractions. E-mails, Facebook, YouTube, surfing the web, nosy coworkers, annoying sales calls, water-cooler gossip, management games, and just plain gabbing can put a dent in the productivity of even the most efficient workers. But for adults with ADD, maintaining long-term productivity at work is an endless struggle—one that often leads to conflict with managers and coworkers, missed promotions, and stalled careers.

In fact, a 2013 study of more than twenty-two thousand adults found that adults with ADD had higher rates of unemployment; were more likely to use recreational drugs; and were more prone to anxiety, depression, eating disorders, and insomnia. In terms of income, adults with ADD can wind up earning as much as $5,000 less per year than their counterparts without ADD.

One client of mine, Danielle, acknowledged that this fit her to a T. Most jobs "begin well," she said. "But then my performance dips. I get spoken to by my manager, which usually leads me to improve my performance for a while."

So I asked, "Why doesn't it last?"

"Somehow, even if I'm improving a bit, it's not long before I make some kind of catastrophic mistake," she said. This results in Danielle being put on probation, or on a "work-management plan," as she referred to it, which is really just a "prefiring exercise."

"Eventually, my lack of ability to be productive ends up in my getting fired," she said. By the time Danielle came to see me, she was twenty-eight years old and had been through this cycle of failure four times. It happens that Danielle, like many adults with ADD, is well aware of the issues that interfere with her productivity at work: inattentiveness, forgetfulness, lack of time management, lack of planning, avoiding mundane tasks, and getting easily distracted. At the same time, she had never learned to create a framework that would help her be more productive on the job.

"I feel like I have to work ten times harder than everyone else just to complete a simple task," she said. "It's so soul destroying to be going through this at this point of my life!"

As painful as her experiences have been, Danielle, as an adult with ADD, is far from alone in this challenge. The first thing I told Danielle was that everything she described was very familiar to me, both as a therapist and as an adult with ADD.

The second thing I suggested was that she learn to practice forgiveness—of herself! The fact of the matter is that the ADD brain develops and works differently that the non-ADD brain. This does not make people with ADD any less smart, witty, or worthy as people than anyone else. However, it does necessitate learning how to work with and around the different wiring associated with ADD.

Many of the world's leading business executives, entertainers, politicians, and business leaders have ADD. A few names include JetBlue CEO, David Neeleman; Virgin Airlines founder, Richard Branson; actor Justin Timberlake; and Olympic swimming champion Michael Phelps. Were these individuals straight A students who fit well into the nice, neat little box of the corporate world? Obviously not. But they did learn how to work to their strengths and develop their productivity so that they would not just succeed—but excel.

In reality, most adults with ADD will not move on to become the next Steve Jobs. However, that does not relegate them to a life of failure and poverty. There are many programs, books, and systems that can help improve productivity. Over the years, I have found two strategies that have been particularly helpful in breaking through the clutter and helping my clients increase their productivity at work.

The first is David Allen's GTD (Getting Things Done) method. You can read his book *Getting Things Done: The Art of Stress-Free Productivity*, which introduces some wonderful concepts that are important for living a productive life. The GTD system includes four basic ideas:

- **Get everything out of your head.** This reduces stress and allows for more creativity. Where do you put the things in your head?
- **Capture all data** that comes from your mind (ideas, goals and things to do) in one place. I use whiteboards and have three in my home. One for short-term goals. One for long-term ideas and goals. And one where I write the things I will accomplish that day. Some people use their iPhone or Android or a small notebook. Simply getting information out of your head frees up more mental space for creativity and relaxation.
- **For items collected during the week,** have one large physical in-box at work and home. Put everything in it. No loose papers. Go through this box once a week, and discard items or act on them.
- **Learn to delegate tasks.** I hired a personal assistant from upwork.com who helps me with mundane work-related tasks. People don't mind hiring someone to clean their house, so why should you have any reluctance to do the same with your job?

After getting a handle on the basics of GTD, read the book *Zen to Done: The Ultimate Simple Productivity System* by Leo Babauta, a much simpler and cleaner version of GTD. For some people, GTD can be overwhelming. *Zen to Done* condenses the information down into simple goals and steps.

One common concern I hear from my clients is that learning to be productive is all well and good, but if it doesn't come with some kind of improvement in focus, the whole exercise is worthless. Certainly, adults with ADD know that difficulty focusing means that getting anything done can take hours when it should take minutes. This is especially true when faced with mundane, boring, or challenging tasks. (It can also be very frustrating for your loved ones who may feel that you have a hard time focusing on them when they are talking.)

Given these challenges, the key to increasing focus is to do only those things that truly excite you. For adults with ADD, motivation is the key to maintaining focus. This may mean hiring an assistant to handle mundane boring tasks that you hate to do.

At the same time, not all of us have the luxury of being able to hire an assistant or working exclusively on things that interest us. Life does tend to get in the way. If and when you find yourself in such a situation, I recommend the following steps to reduce distractions, which will automatically improve focus:

1. Software helps. There are apps out there that can actually make your computer a less distracting place. I personally like the Focus Booster app, which also has the ability to block certain websites at certain times. The Pomodoro Timer is another great website that helps you maintain focus for longer periods of time.
2. Change your location. Try moving to a coffee shop for a while. I love working at Starbucks when I have boring tasks to complete. The buzz of the coffee shop actually increases my motivation, and I set a goal of only working on one task.

3. Make your plan; work your plan. Planning your day, writing down the three things to accomplish that day, and keeping that plan in front of you, can help you focus throughout your hours at work. Many adults with ADD think they can keep everything in their head. This is a mistake. Research finds that once we move beyond two complicated tasks, our brains shift into overload, and we begin to lose track of our original priorities. So write it down.

4. Reward yourself. Finally, as the saying goes, all work and no play make Jack a dull boy. Having something enjoyable to look forward to can often help adults with ADD get over the hump of completing boring tasks so they can move on to the stuff they truly enjoy. Tie your mundane boring task to a reward—like getting a cookie from the cookie jar when you finish your report for work.

Is maintaining focus and productivity a challenge for adults with ADD? Absolutely. But as this lesson shows, there are steps you can take to work with these challenges and take control of your workday. With our careers playing such an important role in our overall self-esteem, any improvements we make from nine to five will automatically have an effect on the rest of our lives as well.

Daily Checklist

1. Set an alarm at 10:30 p.m. to wind down before bed.
2. Buy a water dispenser, and place it nearby.
3. Read *The Zone Diet* by Barry Sears to learn how to regulate glucose levels.
4. Find an exercise plan that is interesting, easy to start, and social.
5. Medication can work for focus and attention, but therapy or coaching is the best long-term solution.
6. Find a meditation center to learn how to meditate.
7. Download the On Second Thought app, and use the "Undo Send" feature in e-mail.
8. When angry, imagine a box around you, and exhale all the air in your lungs.
9. Join a mastermind group to avoid toxic shame and fear of failure.
10. Find a personal and spiritual-growth community that offers you helpful feedback and caring support.
11. Politely decline large projects or tasks where success is not guaranteed. Follow through on small ones to build trust.
12. Say "No" out loud to yourself when you find yourself doing "one more thing."
13. Have a phrase ready ("I would love to, but...") to use when someone asks you to do something.
14. Read *Getting Things Done* and *Zen To Done*. Also use the Pomodoro Technique.

Daily Quiz

What is a good way to be more productive?

a) Use the Pomodoro Technique.
b) Write down three tasks to complete each day.
c) Give yourself a reward after each mundane task.

Correct Answer: a, b, and c

Managing E-mail

I f there is one area where adults with ADD can truly feel they are not alone, it is in e-mail overload. Few people—whether they have Adult ADD or not—can claim to have mastered complete control over their inboxes. For most workers in the information age, time off is never really "off," and vacations are never really vacations, as we find ourselves constantly checking our e-mails and texts for the next new message.

What most of us know from personal experience is now backed up by research. Studies show that e-mail takes up 23 percent of the average employee's workday. Did you know the average worker checks his or her e-mail thirty-six times an hour? And that's just the average worker. That leaves a whole lot of room for the rest of us, who may be spending much more time on e-mail than we care to admit.

The problems associated with e-mail go beyond the simple distraction. Consider this fun fact: minor distractions, e-mail included, can rob us of at least twenty minutes of focus before we regain momentum on the more important task at hand. And if that were not bad enough, e-mail overload actually lowers your IQ! An experiment conducted at the University of London found that people lose as many as ten IQ points when they allow their work to be interrupted by seemingly benign distractions like e-mails and text messages.

In the name of full disclosure, there is yet another reason why e-mail is so difficult to control: frankly, it's fun. The dopamine rush associated with clicking an e-mail is, literally, addictive. Who knows what treasures could be found behind the next e-mail or text message? Checking e-mail allows those of us with Adult ADD to enjoy a full day of immediate gratification! Staying on task? Who wants that?

Despite having ADD, one of my clients has a high-level job at a Fortune 1000 company. She described what it's like for her to try to take control of the overwhelming number of e-mails she receives each day.

"Being at or near the top of your organization, everyone wants a piece of you," she said. "So they send you e-mails. It makes you feel important! But I get over one hundred real e-mails a day!" She went on to do a quick calculation of the kind of time this takes out of her schedule. "At three minutes apiece, it will take five hours just to read and respond to all of those e-mails!" She also did a thought experiment to calculate just how much e-mail overload was costing her company in real dollars. It was too frightening for her to contemplate, she said.

With regard to something as massive as e-mail overload, I warn my clients beforehand not to expect perfection. The idea of a tightly managed e-mail-checking schedule, with an empty, pristine inbox is something few people achieve—and it may not be worth the effort in the first place. The key is to make things manageable and simple. Simple equals sustainable. The more complex the process, the harder it is to sustain over the long haul.

The first problem with e-mail is simply the number of incoming messages. Instead of manually clicking and deleting, the good news is that there is a tool to help you. I recommend using Unroll. me. This great, free service helps you unsubscribe in bulk to all those e-mail newsletters you once thought were so important. The simple act of "unrolling" from all of your newsletters will give your inbox a cleaner and more manageable feel.

While your e-mail is cleaner, I do not subscribe the "Inbox Zero" approach. I think this is a futile effort and not productive for us adults with ADD. Instead, think of your e-mail as a giant living database that you can search for information using the search box of your e-mail program. That is why you don't ever want to delete e-mails. Just let them live on in your e-mail database.

The best way to keep important incoming e-mails under control is to act quickly. One of my favorite mantras is "Do It Now!" I know that if I don't deal with an important or urgent e-mail when it comes in, it will likely be gone from my memory. Then it gets lost in a huge pile of other e-mails that come in. Even a short response is better than none. Responding immediately keeps the communication alive and sends a subtle message to the recipient that you are accountable and can be trusted.

I often will e-mail a short response followed by the words: "What do you think?" or " "What are your thoughts?" This puts the ball back in their court and is an effective way of getting a reminder (from them in the form of a reply) that this matter is still in play.

For very important e-mail responses, where I want to know the outcome and track the progress of something, I will bcc myself this short e-mailed response with a special e-mail address I set up with the words "follow-up" in it. For example: george.sachs.followup@gmail.com. I have set up a filter to channel all e-mails sent to this address into a folder called "@FollowUp." I put the @ before "followup" so that is appears at the top of the e-mail folders, which are listed alphabetically. Periodically check this folder to see if tasks or e-mail chains are completed. I uncheck completed items, rather than deleting them, so that they are no longer shown in this folder but still live in my e-mail database. This should only be used for those e-mails you definitely want to follow up with and for which you need to know a response.

I don't really recommend other folders as this creates more confusion. Keep it simple with one folder called "@Followup" that you check daily.

Two other great free apps that help you gain control over your e-mails are Right Inbox and Boomerang. These apps allow you to delay e-mails and reschedule them to return to your inbox when you have more time to deal with them. The Inbox app by Gmail has a similar feature. Imagine not receiving e-mails until *you* decide you want to deal with them! I find this tool extremely helpful in terms of time management. But don't overuse these systems, as you will become overwhelmed with incoming e-mail that you keep putting off. Use these for e-mails that require much more thought than a simple response. Or when you're out of the office and can't respond immediately. The other great feature of these apps is that you can send an e-mail in the future. I find this helpful when I'm up at 3:00 a.m., working on e-mails, but I don't want my clients to know—so I schedule the e-mails to be sent at a reasonable hour on a weekday.

Finally, do not feel pressured to achieve perfection. Instead, recognize that we live in a world where e-mail is here to stay, and that pretty much everyone struggles with this challenge. Nevertheless, you are not helpless. Implementing these few steps will take you a long way toward clearing your inbox—and your mind—of unnecessary clutter. And that will open up a whole new world of possibilities to being more creative and productive in your career.

Daily Checklist

1. Set an alarm at 10:30 p.m. to wind down before bed.
2. Buy a water dispenser, and place it nearby.
3. Read *The Zone Diet* by Barry Sears to learn how to regulate glucose levels.
4. Find an exercise plan that is interesting, easy to start, and social.
5. Medication can work for focus and attention, but therapy or coaching is the best long-term solution.
6. Find a meditation center to learn how to meditate.
7. Download the On Second Thought app, and use the "Undo Send" feature in e-mail.
8. When angry, imagine a box around you, and exhale all the air in your lungs.
9. Join a mastermind group to avoid toxic shame and fear of failure.
10. Find a personal and spiritual-growth community that offers you helpful feedback and caring support.
11. Politely decline large projects or tasks where success is not guaranteed. Follow through on small ones to build trust.
12. Say "No" out loud to yourself when you find yourself doing "one more thing."
13. Have a phrase ready ("I would love to, but...") to use when someone asks you to do something.
14. Read *Getting Things Done* and *Zen To Done*. Also, use the Pomodoro Technique.

15. Filter a new e-mail address you set up to go into a new "@Followup" folder. Then bcc yourself using this e-mail address on all important e-mails that require follow-up.

Daily Quiz

What is the best way to manage very important e-mail?

a) Delete it.
b) Respond immediately with a short response. Include the phrase, "What are your thoughts?"
c) Respond to e-mail, and bcc yourself at a newly created e-mail address just for following up. Filter this e-mail address into a folder called "@Followup."

Correct Answer: b and c

Day 20 & 21: Weekend Review

Reputation Management

Manage your reputation by being accountable. Deliver on small acts of accountability. Offer to take out the garbage or wash the dishes and actually follow through. Notice the impact of your small act of accountability on the relationship. For larger commitments, feel free to say no. Or if you have to do something, manage expectations by setting realistic deadlines.

Time Management

Time management is relationship management. When we are late, we continue the toxic shame cycle in ourselves and inspire distrust in the other. Overcome "One-More-Thing-Itis" by saying no to yourself out loud the minute you start to do one more thing before walking out the door. When you are on time, notice how positive the feelings are in you.

Overcommitment

Reject the urge to constantly prove your worth by overcommitting (and then failing or coming up short). Simply say no. The power of this word will garner respect in others. Remember what Warren Buffett said: "The difference between successful people and really successful people is that really successful people say no to almost everything."

Productivity

Try these techniques to become more productive. Write down three tasks to do each day on a whiteboard hung in a visible location. Use software like a Pomorodo timer (tomato-timer.com) and Focus Me (focusme.com). Reward yourself after each mundane task with a reward.

Managing E-mail

The key to a managing e-mail is threefold. One, reduce incoming e-mail using a service called Unroll.me. Two, respond immediately, even with a short response, to all e-mails requiring a response. If it's very important for you or the other person, bcc yourself using a special e-mail address you set up. Three, filter this e-mail address into a new folder called @Followup. Check this folder each day to see if important e-mails were dealt with appropriately.

DAY 22
Procrastination

I can't seem to get going and complete
even the easiest of tasks. It's like I'm
stuck in the mud all the time.
—JOHN, TAMPA

Everyone procrastinates some of the time. It's part of human nature to put off today what we can do tomorrow. For people struggling with Adult ADD, however, procrastination becomes a way of life. It starts at a young age—waiting until the last minute to do a book report or staying up all night to finish that term paper. It's not just school or work assignments that we avoid. It can be something as simple as folding the clothes or changing a diaper. Even the smallest of tasks takes a monumental effort. Why is this? Others seem to go through life banging things off their to-do list, while those of us with Adult ADD can't seem to get one thing done all day.

After impulsivity, procrastination is the second most intractable symptom of Adult ADD. For me, if there is something boring or large, with many steps, to accomplish, it almost feels painful to move and get started. Like moving a beached whale back to the ocean. Of course, everyone struggles with procrastination to some degree (thus the title of the famous productivity book, *Getting Things Done* by David Allen), but adults with ADD seem to suffer to a greater frequency and greater degree than others.

This is why Russell Barkley, PhD, a leading scientist in the field, refers to Adult ADD as motivation deficit disorder.

The good news is that there are steps you can take to get a handle on the procrastination monster. But before we jump to solutions, it's a good idea to take a look at what it feels like to be inside the head of someone with Adult ADD. No two brains—or people—are the same, but there are enough similarities in terms of how the ADD brain functions to give us a sense of what's really going on.

We all know what it's like to have a number of voices inside our head pushing us in different directions. Picture the following scene: You're driving down the road of life with two very different backseat drivers clamoring for attention. One is the "Instant Gratification Monkey" and the other is the "Critical Mother-in-Law." The Instant Gratification Monkey, also known as the Monkey Brain, is just that—an annoying, persistent, and convincing pest that wants what it wants, and it wants it now. That's the voice that pipes up when you're working on your taxes due tomorrow and says, "Hey, let's take a trip down memory land and see if our ex is still on Facebook. Or better yet, let's look for every single person we ever even thought about dating in school and look them up!"

The Critical Mother-in-Law, on the other hand, is the voice of rational disapproval. "You do know there are only five hours until your taxes are due, don't you? Most people are able to keep the Critical Mother-in-Law at bay until she brings in a very important ally known as the "Panic Monster." Once the Panic Monster is summoned, most people recognize that they better buckle down if they don't want to wind up in a world of hurt. For regular folks, this realization eventually scares them enough to get moving. However, for people with Adult ADD, bringing in the Panic Monster is not always a guarantee of getting things done.

To make matters worse, those of us with Adult ADD don't even have the luxury of using the same excuses as everyone else. This is because by the time we've reached our midtwenties, there is no more credit left on the "excuse card." To those with Adult ADD, there is little hope of trying to convince our teachers, bosses, friends, family, or lovers that the reason we procrastinate is that the work is "boring" or "no fun."

To add insult to injury, medication doesn't always help. Most ADD medications help increase focus. This can be poison for someone trying not to procrastinate, because the meds may simply help us focus on anything and everything except the task we're supposed to complete!

For some adults with ADD, the habit of procrastination is a by-product of the talents we discovered as children. It was those very talents—the things that made us feel good about ourselves—that got us in the most trouble! So, the child with ADD who is a gifted artist or musician may have learned to take refuge in those activities in order to avoid buckling down on his homework in subjects that were more difficult to master. Once out of school and into "real life," adults with ADD may expect everything to come as easily as the things they are good at. This can turn into a kind of perfectionism that demands all or nothing. If something is more difficult to complete, it immediately goes into the "nothing" column, and the door is open to distraction and procrastination.

Despite the fact that procrastination is likely to be a lifelong challenge, there are strategies you can incorporate into your life to increase motivation to get tasks done quickly. I go through a multistep questioning process with my clients to get to the bottom of their procrastination and find a solution.

Here are the questions:

1. Are you forcing your square peg into a round hole? Or are you truly doing what you love?
2. Are you "shoulding" on yourself, believing you should be able to complete a task or project, when you simply are unable?
3. Have you set goals for yourself?
4. Have you externalized the motivation?
5. What is your reward for your efforts?
6. If you have to do something, are you "chunking" it?

In this lesson, I will briefly describe each of these questions. Later lessons will focus on each one in depth.

Square Peg in a Round Hole

If you are spending your life procrastinating on tasks, then it's probably a good bet that you don't enjoy your job or life all that much. This is why I ask this question first. Could you be doing something more interesting that fits with your unique ADD personality? If something is hard or boring to do, it's important to look at the reasons why this task or assignment keeps getting relegated to the back burner. Maybe it's something you would be better of jettisoning from your life? Thus, a good portion of the challenge of procrastination can be avoided by arranging life in a way that truly fits your skills, goals, and personality. Once you are doing things you enjoy and are naturally good at, procrastination becomes less of a problem.

Don't Should on Me

Often those of us with Adult ADD feel we have to do something, and, when we can't, we beat ourselves up. We say: "I should be able to do my taxes. It's so easy with Quicken." Or, "I should be able to do my laundry...just throw the clothes in the washing machine." The problem is that we procrastinate and keep telling ourselves we should be doing it, but never do. This perpetuates the cycle of shame and failure. What I recommend is simply delegating, offloading, or paying someone to do what we can't do (but think we should be able to do). If we accept our limitations (the key part) and the challenges of ADHD, we free ourselves from the "shoulds." Delegate boring tasks, hire someone to do your cleaning and laundry, and don't force yourself to do things you simply can't.

Setting Goals

Much of the time we procrastinate because we don't have clearly defined, reachable, and measurable goals. With a goal, we can visualize success and then plan a road map to success. It's very important to find out what you want (not what others want for you or what society wants for you), and then chart a clear path to get there. Once this path is complete, motivation will increase, and then procrastination becomes more manageable with the following steps.

Externalize the Motivation

Sometimes it may be impossible to ignore or delegate certain tasks—like going to the gym or practicing the piano for a major recital. I used to work at Juilliard, the famous arts conservatory, coaching and providing therapy to its students. Many of these students had Adult ADD and disliked practicing. Success for them meant they must practice and achieve the highest levels of competency in their instrument. I recommended they externalize the motivation. What does this mean?

Russell Barkley, PhD, says that the internal voice that tells us what to do, and when, is weak in those with ADD. Knowing this, we have to look outside ourselves for motivation. This is what I mean by externalizing the motivation—finding external cues or triggers to increase our desire to complete a task.

For the students at Juilliard, I recommended that they enter a musical contest, post the date of the contest on their wall, and set a goal of being prepared for that date. Now the need to practice is externalized, and their competitive nature and the goal of winning, will propel them to practice more and not procrastinate. How can you externalize your goals? Hire a trainer at the gym? Enter a screenwriting contest to force yourself to write that first draft?

The Power of Habit

Charles Duhigg wrote a great book on the subject of making habits stick: *The Power of Habit*. For me the key ingredient was the reward that follows the behavior to cement the habit. Without a reward at the end, the desired behavior doesn't stick and we lose interest. What is the task you need to do? Clean the car every month from all the crumbs the kids leave behind? This sounds boring and tedious. So first think of the reward you'll give yourself each time you clean the car. Perhaps there's an ice cream shop near the car wash. Think of giving yourself a treat after the task, and, all of a sudden, getting started doesn't seem that hard.

Chunking

If you absolutely must get something done, and you've externalized the motivation and built in a reward, then I aslo recommend breaking the project into small pieces. For example, if you have to clean the garage—and it's something you really hate—then consider dividing the project into ten discrete tasks. It's much easier to get started on one small task (throwing away the junk), than to get started on the larger project (cleaning the entire garage). In addition, control your procrastination by setting limits on how long you actually work. Don't set a goal of working for two hours straight. Set a goal of working twenty to twenty-five minutes straight, followed by a break. Research shows that most people can only focus for twenty to twenty-five minutes before a break is needed. Use a timer (online at Tomato-Timer.com) and set it for twenty-five minutes. Take a break for five minutes and let your mind refresh and recharge.

Bottom line: if you're prone to procrastination, follow these six steps to success. Don't be a square peg in a round hole. Find your life's passions. Don't "should" on yourself—delegate or hire someone to do what you don't want to do. Set a goal; build in a reward; and externalize the motivation by hiring a coach, joining a team, or entering a contest of your own choosing to motivate you to move forward. These steps will help your internal ADD voice go from weak to powerful.

Daily Checklist

1. Set an alarm at 10:30 p.m. to wind down before bed.
2. Buy a water dispenser, and place it nearby.
3. Read *The Zone Diet* by Barry Sears to learn how to regulate glucose levels.
4. Find an exercise plan that is interesting, easy to start, and social.
5. Medication can work for focus and attention, but therapy or coaching is the best long-term solution.
6. Find a meditation center to learn how to meditate.
7. Download the On Second Thought app, and use the "Undo Send" feature in e-mail.
8. When angry, imagine a box around you, and exhale all the air in your lungs.
9. Join a mastermind group to avoid toxic shame and fear of failure.
10. Find a personal and spiritual-growth community that offers you helpful feedback and caring support.
11. Politely decline large projects or tasks where success is not guaranteed. Follow through on small ones to build trust.
12. Say "No" out loud to yourself when you find yourself doing "one more thing."
13. Have a phrase ready ("I would love to, but...") to use when someone asks you to do something.
14. Read *Getting Things Done* and *Zen To Done*. Also, use the Pomodoro Technique.

15. Filter a new e-mail address you set up to go into a new "@Followup" folder. Then bcc yourself using this e-mail address on all important e-mails that require follow-up.

16. Externalize the motivation by hiring a coach, working on a team, or setting time-bound goals. Don't "should" on yourself by thinking you can do it alone.

Daily Quiz

What is one way to manage procrastination?

a) Make sure you're not a square peg in a round hole, doing a job you hate or find boring.
b) Wait until the internal feeling of motivation naturally arises.
c) Externalize the motivation, by hiring a coach or trainer to motivate you in areas where you need extra support.

Correct Answer: a and c

DAY 23
Don't Should on Yourself

What screws us up most in life is the picture
in our head of how it is supposed to be.
—ANONYMOUS

once had a client who was a medical doctor. Despite his academic achievements, he struggled with Adult ADD, and he quickly found himself procrastinating with the paperwork associated with his practice. In the modern world of healthcare, a lot of important report writing and documentation needs to be completed during the examination, when he is supposed to be present for his patients and their concerns. It drove him crazy.

Being a therapist and no stranger to government-mandated paperwork myself, I commiserated with him, acknowledging that many doctors today find themselves focusing more on the computer terminal in the room than on the patient in front of them.

While we were engaged in some back-and-forth attempts at problem solving, I asked him to think about delegating the note writing to a virtual assistant or a nurse in the room with him. That way he could focus on the task of connecting with his patients, meet their needs, and still make sure the proper paperwork was filed on time and accurately.

Initially my client thought this was a good idea. And then the "shoulds" took over. "But I should be able to take the notes and talk to a patient," he said. What he meant was that if he was truly a good doctor, he would be able to do all the tasks necessary for the job, including mundane paperwork. Not being able to do this made him feel like a failure.

Many adults with ADD suffer from this streak of perfectionism, leading to avoidance and procrastination of necessary tasks.

One of the first psychotherapists to explore the debilitating effects of perfectionism was Karen Horney. Born in Germany in the late nineteen hundreds, Dr. Horney eventually immigrated to America, where she developed her own school of psychotherapy. She is perhaps best known for introducing the term the "tyranny of should." According to Horney, many people go through life needlessly suffering, because they carry two unrealistic and inaccurate views of who they truly are. There is the "ideal self," which is the person we think we should be (essentially Superman), and the real self or the person we think we are (essentially Homer Simpson). Even though our real selves may be quite accomplished and successful—my client became a doctor, after all—whatever we do pales in comparison to the ideal self, which constantly reminds us of what we "should" be doing.

This leads us to set up completely unrealistic goals—only to have them crash and burn on the shores of "reality."

The result is that many people wind up walking around in a cloud of self-hatred. And for people with Adult ADD, the whole formula is on steroids. The "shoulds" are more demanding; more unrealistic; and more distracting, damaging, and devastating to our self-esteem. Many adults with ADD find that, after a while, they simply end up avoiding work or tasks they find too intimidating. Or they waste precious time seeking the perfect strategy to do everything they think they need to do, as impossible as that may be. Even worse in terms of actually making progress, people with Adult ADD may assume that if they can just become "perfect," all of the criticism and pain they grew up with will magically disappear.

Obviously clinging to these illusions will not bring about any lasting change. However, that does not mean that there is no hope! Quite the contrary. With a little bit of self-compassion, people with Adult ADD can free themselves from the "tyranny of the shoulds," and make positive changes in their lives.

The first step is to stop "shoulding" on yourself.

The key is to admit that you have both weaknesses and strengths and to focus your energy on your strengths. This is similar to the alcoholic who must admit he or she has a problem. From that honest admission of the truth, real change can occur. The same is true with Adult ADD. Once we admit we have deficits, we can begin the process of change.

The doctor in the example I gave earlier was great with people—which was a real strength. He was, however, too focused on his weaknesses and "shoulded" all over himself. With coaching, he realized he can spend more time with his patients and enhance the quality of their care by using his strengths. Avoiding his weaknesses, he learned to delegate the report writing to a virtual nurse. A brilliant use of technology for the adult with ADD.

What are your weaknesses? One of mine is doing boring, detail-oriented work that must be done every week, like book-keeping, payroll, and accounting. I recognize these are not my strengths, so I delegate them to others. Now I feel like a one-minute manager, and the self-loathing thoughts that I should do those tasks and the mistakes that come when I do those tasks it are gone.

Here are the three steps to moving beyond your "shoulds" and accepting your strengths.

- Assess your strengths and weaknesses. Know thyself. Look at areas of weakness and try to organize your day around things you are good at, rather than becoming obsessed with your perceived failings. For example, instead of looking at the laundry piling up that you can't seem to get to, hire a cleaning person to come in and do it for you. You may need to cut back on your Starbucks coffee consumption to pay for it, but it will get done.
- Focus on the big picture. Don't be afraid to delegate. To the adult-ADD mind, everything is important. Therefore, the key to better functioning is to decide what is important and what is *more* important. To go back to our doctor and his office. Paperwork is important. Without it, he will find himself in hot water with the managed care organization or with the government. But focusing on

his patients is *more* important. Decluttering the garage is important. No one wants to look at a mess. But spending time with your spouse and family is *more* important than getting lost in the garage for several hours on a weekend. Imagine achieving *both* goals by hiring someone to clean the garage while you take the kids to the park or go for a walk with your spouse! (No, *not* the other way around!)

- Redefine Success. To someone caught in the tyranny of the "shoulds," success is basically impossible. That is because there is no end to the number of "shoulds" a person can put on his or her to-do list for life. As the saying goes, you can never be too thin or too rich. In truth that ought to be a phrase people take as a cute joke—not a commandment from on high. Once a person frees himself from the "shoulds," success becomes much easier to achieve, because it's not based on being perfect. Instead success is based on working with your unique nature, rather than against it.

If I could leave my Adult ADD clients with one piece of advice when it comes to this challenge, this would be it: stop "shoulding" yourself, accept your weaknesses, focus on your strengths, and start enjoying life!

Daily Checklist

1. Set an alarm at 10:30 p.m. to wind down before bed.
2. Buy a water dispenser, and place it nearby.
3. Read *The Zone Diet* by Barry Sears to learn how to regulate glucose levels.
4. Find an exercise plan that is interesting, easy to start, and social.
5. Medication can work for focus and attention, but therapy or coaching is the best long-term solution.
6. Find a meditation center to learn how to meditate.
7. Download the On Second Thought app, and use the "Undo Send" feature in e-mail.
8. When angry, imagine a box around you, and exhale all the air in your lungs.
9. Join a mastermind group to avoid toxic shame and fear of failure.
10. Find a personal- or spiritual-growth community that offers you helpful feedback and caring support.
11. Politely decline large projects or tasks where success is not guaranteed. Follow through on small ones to build trust.
12. Say "No" out loud to yourself when you find yourself doing "one more thing."
13. Have a phrase ready ("I would love to, but...") to use when someone asks you to do something.
14. Read *Getting Things Done* and *Zen To Done*. Also, use the Pomodoro Technique.

15. Filter a new e-mail address you set up to go into a new "@Followup" folder. Then bcc yourself using this e-mail address on all important e-mails that require follow-up.

16. Externalize the motivation by hiring a coach, working on a team, or setting time-bound goals. Don't "should" on yourself by thinking you can do it alone.

17. Accept your weaknesses, and delegate difficult tasks.

Daily Quiz

What is the best way to handle tasks that you think you should do, but don't?

a) Just suck it up and work harder.
b) Delegate or hire people to do difficult or boring tasks.
c) You should be able to do anything if you put your mind to it.

Correct Answer: b

DAY 24
Square Peg, Round Hole

I'm really bored and unmotivated at my job and can't seem to get the work done. I'm generally happy outside of 9:00 a.m. to 5:00 p.m. so I don't think I'm depressed. I just struggle to get stuff done. How can I become more motivated?
—PERRY, CHICAGO

Adults with ADD often find themselves in a constant struggle to overcome a lack of motivation or energy to get their work done at school or at the office. By the time they come to my practice, they are nearly at the end of their rope. The most common complaint I hear is that they that just can't get things done. No matter how hard they try to focus, they can't finish their work. Usually this pattern has been in place since they were children, and by the time these individuals reach college or the working world, they can site a long list of failures. The history of their interactions with professors or bosses is riddled with poor write-ups and even worse interpersonal relations. With their heads hung low, my clients with Adult ADD almost always blame themselves for their failures. They believe they "should" be able to do their work, like everyone else. All of this leaves them in tears, broken over the fact that they have been left behind or are on the road to a lifetime of failure.

That's a heavy load to carry through life!

Instead of letting my clients lose themselves in the dark pit of low self-esteem, I tell them to lift their heads! And if you're reading this and have Adult ADD, I am telling you the same thing. Lift your head! You are not the problem. The problem is that you are a square peg trying to fit in a round hole.

Instead of working to your strengths, you try to conform to someone else's idea of who you should be. In short, you are trying to be something you're not. Naturally this is a recipe for disaster. Do you feel like a square peg in a round hole? I did earlier in my career. Being someone's administrative assistant was not going to work for me, or my boss. After finding a career that called upon my strengths, I started having more success.

Not too long ago, I met with Richard, a twenty-one-year-old man attending a liberal arts college, who came to my office to try to "cure" his ADD. As I listened to him, it was immediately clear to me that Richard was very bright and had a lot of talents. However, his intelligence seemed to be of little help when it came to succeeding at school. His grades were far below his potential, and yet all he could tell me was that he "lacked motivation" and "couldn't get anything done."

Richard was one of the classic "should" cases—and in my opinion, he was right. He "should" have been able to get his work done. He "should" have been succeeding at college. He "should" have been on the road to a great career. He was no longer a child—so what was his problem?

Sound familiar?

His problem was that he was focusing on the wrong "should."

Instead of falling into the trap of believing himself to be a failure, Richard "should" have realized that as an Adult with ADD, his brain truly was wired differently. Understanding this one fact could have changed Richard's entire life trajectory. It could have helped him change the kinds of subjects, tasks, or assignments he chose from those he found boring to those that held his attention. Acknowledging, embracing, and working with the unique way his brain functions could have helped Richard remove all the damaging "shoulds" he had lived with until then.

Adults with ADD really do struggle with motivation, because the mechanism in the brain that controls this trait is faulty. It simply doesn't have enough juice to keep the focus and motivation high for uninteresting tasks. After working with Richard to help him understand this simple concept, I recommended that he transfer to a school where he could tap into subjects that truly excited him. In Richard's case, his passion was for film. So I recommended he go to film school—a place where he would be stimulated by the many, varied elements that go into making a film. Ultimately, finding something that truly interested him was the key to unlocking Richard's potential. He eventually transferred and is enjoying his newfound love for school, which he told me now feels like freedom instead of drudgery. He is truly on his way.

That's all well and good, you may say. But what about me? What about people who are silently suffering with Adult ADD and don't even know how to begin searching for the right interests or career path for themselves.

Let's start with some key principles. As an adult with ADD, the first thing you have to understand is that you are not the only one struggling with these issues. Studies have found that ADD is the second-ranking disability among college students, with as many as 11 percent of students diagnosed with this condition. For this group of people, the fundamental task of choosing a career path can turn into a protracted nightmare. Despite all the challenges and negative feedback they may have received growing up, children and teenagers with ADD live in a fairly protected environment. They know what comes next. It's just a matter of getting through the path that has been laid out for them—even if it's filled with bumps and blows to their self-esteem.

Once they reach college, these young adults with ADD face the challenge of having to decide, perhaps for the first time, what the next step in their lives will be. To be sure, this could be said about nearly everyone transitioning from high school to college to the working world. But for adults with ADD, problems with time management, lack of focus, failure to complete assignments, difficulty scheduling appointments, low tolerance for frustration, and all of their other difficulties with executive functioning come rushing to the foreground. These problems not only affect school work, they affect the ability to properly evaluate how to choose a major or an appropriate career path. All of this creates a perfect storm of confusion and frustration, which is much more pronounced than it is for those without ADD.

This ongoing failure initiates a vicious cycle of negative self-talk, lack of confidence, and a sense of worthlessness. Is it any wonder that by the time an adult with ADD reaches the workforce, he or she is a crisis waiting to happen?

To make matters worse, adults with ADD, having failed to choose a career that fits their personality, will more often than not just choose anything handy. The latest fad will do—because deep down inside they know that they will eventually fail at that, too.

If this sounds familiar, I am here to tell you that it does not have to be this way!

As I mentioned before, the problems adults with ADD have in the workplace all come down to the idea of trying to fit a square peg in a round hole. My job is to help you get out of that kind of thinking and open yourself up to discovering your true calling. Once a person with ADD has done that, the working world can once again be filled with hope and enthusiasm.

The first thing I recommend for my clients is to forget about drawing up an extensive list of their flaws. It's much more productive to concentrate on strengths and preferences instead. The following questions can help you begin to uncover some of the hidden dreams you may have thought were beyond reach.

- What are you good at? That sounds like a simple enough question, but you would be surprised by how many of my clients cannot answer that question. This is the place to start. What do you do best? Spend some time thinking about activities and tasks that give you joy and at which you excel. Stop spending time trying to get good at what you're no good at. Instead, listen to the inner voice that tells you where your true talents lie and give yourself permission—finally—to develop those interests.

- Of the things you are good at, which do you like the most? For many adults with ADD this can be tricky. Everything on the list seems great! How can anyone choose? Does this mean forever? For this exercise, I tell clients that they can have multiple lists, but spend some time jotting down those things that really speak to you. Eventually a pattern will emerge. Go with the pattern to see the three, four, or five favorite things you can see yourself doing in the working world.

- Where can you improve? The purpose of this question is not to overload you with self-help assignments. Instead, gaining an understanding of what you are not so good at will tell you several important things when it comes to working. First, it will help you clarify your career path by showing you what does not work. Second, it will tell you which tasks you will need to delegate to succeed. There is no sin in realizing that you don't have to do everything—and the truth is you should not even try. I know a very successful person who works in sales and marketing—even though she hates making cold calls! For most people in sales, not being good at cold calls is a recipe for disaster. However, in this case, my friend has figured out that she is good enough to know what needs to be said, who needs to be called, and how to create a system she can delegate. The same holds true for adults with ADD. If you are not good at something, and it's vital to your job, find a way to delegate that responsibility to someone who can do it. You'll be hailed as a hero for your leadership! Knowing where you can improve also shows you where you need a mentor. Rather than pushing you out the door, your boss may respect the fact that you come to him or her openly with a request for mentoring. It shows you are looking to improve your skills.

- What are you most proud of in your work life? This answer to this question will also reveal important clues about your true calling. We tend to be proud of achievements that are the result of a lot of blood, sweat, and tears. People are only willing to put in significant time to things that draw their passion.

Spending time exploring these questions can help you create a mental map of a career path that plays to your strengths. Instead of forcing yourself to conform to some idealized vision of what you "should" be, the answers to these questions will help you realize that there is nothing wrong with you that can't be fixed by knowing where you belong.

Daily Checklist

1. Set an alarm at 10:30 p.m. to wind down before bed.
2. Buy a water dispenser, and place it nearby.

3. Read *The Zone Diet* by Barry Sears to learn how to regulate glucose levels.

4. Find an exercise plan that is interesting, easy to start, and social.

5. Medication can work for focus and attention, but therapy or coaching is the best long-term solution.

6. Find a meditation center to learn how to meditate.

7. Download the On Second Thought app, and use the "Undo Send" feature in e-mail.

8. When angry, imagine a box around you, and exhale all the air in your lungs.

9. Join a mastermind group to avoid toxic shame and fear of failure.

10. Find a personal and spiritual-growth community that offers you helpful feedback and caring support.

11. Politely decline large projects or tasks where success is not guaranteed. Follow through on small ones to build trust.

12. Say "No" out loud to yourself when you find yourself doing "one more thing."

13. Have a phrase ready ("I would love to, but...") to use when someone asks you to do something.

14. Read *Getting Things Done* and *Zen To Done*. Also, use the Pomodoro Technique.

15. Filter a new e-mail address you set up to go into a new "@Followup" folder. Then bcc yourself using this e-mail address on all important e-mails that require follow-up.

16. Externalize the motivation by hiring a coach, working on a team, or setting time-bound goals. Don't "should" on yourself by thinking you can do it alone.
17. Accept your weaknesses, and delegate difficult tasks.
18. Ask yourself if you're a "square peg in a round hole." If so, it's time to consider a new job or career.

Daily Quiz

What is a possible reason for your procrastination and low motivation?

a) No job will be perfect for you. Suck it up.
b) You're lazy and need to work harder.
c) You're not using your real talents.

Correct Answer: c

DAY 25
Closing the Loops

*I start so many things and don't finish anything.
There's a mess of unfinished projects all over
my house. It stresses me out and makes
me feel like I can't accomplish anything.*
—HENRY L., SAN FRANCISCO

recently asked one of my clients to describe what his work day was like. He told me that most of the time his days are one big blur of the multitasking hell. First, he might find himself drumming his fingers on his desk while he scans his e-mails on his computer screen. At the same time, he could be speaking on the phone about an important issue with an executive halfway around the world, barely paying attention. Meanwhile, he becomes so engrossed in multitasking that he forgets important appointments, even when his computer is set to remind him just fifteen minutes before he has to leave, make a call, or turn his attention to something else. The most depressing thing for my client is that he readily admits this could go on all day, almost every day of the week.

Weekends are no better. "I sit down to work on my to-do list, and then I remember that I need to water the new trees in the back yard," he said, describing a typical Saturday. "This makes me realize I need to put the rake up, which makes me take it to the garage, where I realize I was going to organize the storage closet, which I start doing, only to realize that I need to change the air filters in the house when I find them in the storage closet, which makes me go to get out the ladder, only to realize I never did put those hooks on the wall to hang the ladder on, which prompts me to hang the hooks on the wall and put the ladder in its place."

This whole process of getting lost like this could eat up a couple hours of his time. "At the end of the day, all I actually might accomplish is putting the hooks on the garage wall. Everything else that popped into my head did not get done, and I am left wondering what the hell just happened to my day. How did it get so late so fast?"

This, my client told me, is supposed to be his day off. Instead of recharging his batteries on the weekend, all he really achieves is exhaustion, so that by the time Monday rolls around, he is already burned out and behind schedule. As a therapist who works with both adults with ADD and those who do not have ADD, I can assure you that ADD-ers are not alone. Anyone can get caught up in the kind of multitasking nightmare my client described. The difference is that non-ADD adults retain the ability to turn things off. They may need some coaching or easy reminders to do this, but if they decide to power down and focus, they can do it fairly easily.

Adults with ADD don't know how to do this. On the one hand, adults with ADD are usually creative, curious and full of energy. This is a great asset. On the other hand, if you can't control this energy and channel it into something productive, it becomes yet another albatross around your neck. By way of comparison, the typical adult without ADD might think of two or three things to do per day that are outside their normal schedule of commitments. The typical adult with ADD will think of five or ten tasks to do per day. Multiply that by a week or a month, and you can quickly see life can become overwhelming for adults with ADD.

In the world of Adult ADD treatment, we call these unfinished projects "open loops." After a while, these open loops start to pile up—and then they take revenge. They start to taunt you, demanding that you finish what you set out to achieve. The problem is that by the time you return to your original projects, you have already lost interest or found yourself wandering in a maze of unfinished projects. Instead of enjoying the fruits of your labor, all that remains is a mess—and usually an expensive mess at that.

Why are adults with ADD so much less able to close their loops than adults without ADD? As is often the case, much of it comes down to the different way the ADD brain functions.

Research shows that, in general, the more data being processed by the brain, the more difficult it is for a person to make rational decisions, manage time, or solve problems. All of the tools needed to finish a task—flexibility, creativity, and the ability to avoid mistakes—require a calm and collected state of mind. However, achieving this state is impossible once the brain senses its circuits are overloading.

The reason for this is that just beneath the executive functioning area of the brain lies the more primitive, reptilian part of the brain. At this level, all that matters is survival. When a person is functioning well, the survival centers of the brain send positive messages to the executive functioning control center. This, in turn, allows the person to feel energized and motivated. Some people call it being in the "zone." Being in the zone is fantastic—but there's a catch. The brain can usually only handle about five "big" decisions at a time. Once a person hits the sixth decision (and beyond), the primitive, survival-focused "reptilian" brain hits the panic button. Instead of joy, fear rules the day. Fear of failure. Fear of being overwhelmed—essentially fear of being eaten up by the monster! Once the fear monster starts running the show, everything that "comes at" a person is interpreted as a threat. There is no time for calm, collected, fluid activity. Instead, the "flight mechanism" is engaged, and the to do-list goes out the window. Because adults with ADD have no pause button on input, they are more susceptible to the fear monster emanating from the reptilian brain. Rather than an exciting project, every open loop is a predator ready to eat us up!

Is all lost? Not at all.

The good news is that both my experience in learning to close my own loops and in working with Adult ADD clients has led me to create a simple strategy that can change your life forever.

The first piece of advice I tell my clients consists of simple steps: Stop. Look. Listen. The moment you find yourself attracted to the next shiny object and tempted to take on yet another great new project, stop. Don't do anything. Put away the credit card.

Don't click on buy. Don't run to the hardware store. Consciously force yourself to stop. Just for a few minutes. It helps to say "stop" or "no" out loud. Russell Barkley, PhD, says that the the inner voice of reason is weaker in adults with ADD. So make the inner voice external and say "no."

Next, look. Take a quick inventory of your current projects. Whether you have them written down on a list (we'll get to that in a moment), or whether you just have a running list in your head, look to see what is going on in terms of your open loops. Any more than three open loops is probably too many.

Finally, listen. Take some time to hear what the excited part of your brain is telling you. Is it realistic? Can you really get it done? Try to listen to other, quieter voices that are warning you not to take on this new commitment. This is different than fear. This is the voice of deeper wisdom telling you there is nothing wrong with slowing down. The goal of the stop, look, and listen process is to help you start to gain control of your thinking by slowing the flow of input to your brain. In other words, the first step in closing your loops is not to open up any unnecessary new ones.

As I mentioned, a good rule of thumb is the rule of three. If you have any more than three open loops—just say no. It does not have to be a forever no. It can be a temporary no. You can tell yourself that you are not permanently killing this wonderful new idea. Instead you are putting it on hold for the time being.

One way to strengthen the stop, look, and listen process is to write down any new project on a whiteboard. Let the idea sit there for a few days, weeks, or months before you decide to move forward. That way, the excited part of your brain gets the satisfaction of seeing and entertaining the idea without forcing you into concrete action.

Once you have begun to master the process of closing the door on new projects, the second step is to close the loop on your existing commitments. For this step I recommend working with a buddy. We also call this "externalizing the motivation." One of my clients used to bemoan the fact that she simply could not finish tasks. Even such mundane things as cleaning out her closet or doing the dishes from the night before would become overwhelming. Then one day a friend happened to be at her house while she was trying to clear out some clutter from a closet. In a fit of desperation, she asked her friend just to be there with her while she went at the task. Somehow having another person there changed her whole approach to the project. Instead of a chore, it became a fun social event. In fact, she did not even need her friend to do any work. Just being there with her to talk and distract her mind while her hands kept busy was enough.

Think of it this way: People hire personal trainers to help them get over the hump and start exercising. Having a buddy with you to close some loops is like having a personal productivity coach. Most people with ADD do not necessarily need advice on how to get things done. What they need is a safe way to be distracted while still staying on task. A task buddy does this wonderfully.

If your buddy cannot be there with you physically, another tactic is to have a friend call at a designated time, let's say the next fifteen minutes. During the time between calls, you can race yourself to see how much of your project you can get down.

Finally, make sure the goals associated with your project are clear and concrete. Setting goals like cleaning the garage or learning how to play harmonica are too vague. A better strategy is to create a specific, short-term, concrete goal that has a clear starting point and, more importantly, a clear end. Instead of cleaning the garage, tell yourself you are filling three boxes and donating them to Goodwill. Instead of "mastering the harmonica," tell yourself you will learn one song. Small loops are much easier to close than big loops. In addition, building a track record of success will motivate you to stay on track.

Is this formula an instant fix? No. Learning to reprogram a lifetime of habits takes time. However, many of my clients find it to be a relatively painless way of learning how to increase their productivity both at work and at home, as well as in other areas of life.

Daily Checklist

1. Set an alarm at 10:30 p.m. to wind down before bed.
2. Buy a water dispenser, and place it nearby.
3. Read *The Zone Diet* by Barry Sears to learn how to regulate glucose levels.
4. Find an exercise plan that is interesting, easy to start, and social.
5. Medication can work for focus and attention, but therapy or coaching is the best long-term solution.
6. Find a meditation center to learn how to meditate.
7. Download the On Second Thought app, and use the "Undo Send" feature in e-mail.
8. When angry, imagine a box around you, and exhale all the air in your lungs.
9. Join a mastermind group to avoid toxic shame and fear of failure.
10. Find a personal and spiritual-growth community that offers you helpful feedback and caring support.
11. Politely decline large projects or tasks where success is not guaranteed. Follow through on small ones to build trust.
12. Say "No" out loud to yourself when you find yourself doing "one more thing."
13. Have a phrase ready ("I would love to, but...") to use when someone asks you to do something.
14. Read *Getting Things Done* and *Zen To Done*. Also, use the Pomodoro Technique.

15. Filter a new e-mail address you set up to go into a new "@Followup" folder. Then bcc yourself using this e-mail address on all important e-mails that require follow-up.
16. Externalize the motivation by hiring a coach, working on a team, or setting time-bound goals. Don't "should" on yourself by thinking you can do it alone.
17. Accept your weaknesses, and delegate difficult tasks.
18. Ask yourself if you're a "square peg in a round hole." If so, it's time to consider a new job or career.
19. Manage the open loops in your life by limiting new ones and working with a buddy, partner, or coach to externalize the motivation to close open loops.

Daily Quiz

What is the best way to manage open loops in your life?

a) Limit starting new projects until the old loops are closed.
b) Just forget about it and move on.
c) Work with a friend or coach to externalize your motivation to close the open loops so you can start new ones.

Correct Answer: a and c

DAY 26
Goal Setting

Sometimes I get lost in not only what I'm doing,
but why I'm doing it. Then all motivation is lost.
— DARCY, ENGLAND

Hockey great Wayne Gretzky said it best: "You miss 100 percent of the shots you don't take."

Are you taking shots on goal? Most of the time, having Adult ADD means living "behind the eight ball." Given the daily challenges with planning, organization, and especially follow-through, the idea of having goals in life may seem almost laughable.

Actually, I should clarify that last statement. Of course, adults with ADD have goals. Lots of them. From conquering the world to making a million dollars to building a better mousetrap. We are the champions of running after the latest shiny object. But pie-in-the-sky dreams are not what I mean by goals. Instead, when I talk to my clients about setting goals, I mean being proactive—rather than constantly reactive—about life.

That's where I usually start to encounter resistance. Rarely do the people who show up in my office have trouble "dreaming big." Instead, their main problem is "dreaming small." The notion of getting out in front of their lives by making a plan, working a plan, and staying with a plan seems too difficult to imagine.

Katie Ledecky is a five-time Olympic gold medalist and nine-time world champion. She has held the world record in the women's 400-, 800-, and 1,500-meter freestyle, and the fastest-ever times in the women's 500-, 1,000-, and 1,650-yard freestyle events. Her achievements also include winning four gold medals at the Rio Olympics in 2016. When asked about how she was able to achieve such stunning success, she put it down to one simple thought: "I pretty much met my goals to the nose."

No one would deny that there are many factors that go into the creation of a gold-medal winning Olympic athlete. Genetics, grit, training, proper coaching, and relentless practice all play a key role. But Katie's regimen included one other "secret ingredient." Each day after practice, Katie and her coach would compare her times to that day's goal. That is why she wasn't surprised that she won the 800-meter freestyle event by eleven seconds over her nearest competitor. (Eleven seconds in swimming is an eternity, by the way.) This was a goal that she trained for, measured herself against each week, and was on track to beat.

Katie's strategy for success is backed by scientific research. A study at Dominican University looked at the success rate of goal-setting. The scientists found that the following three practices led to the most success in achieving goals:

1. Write the goal down.
2. Make a public commitment to a friend.
3. Share progress with this friend.

It just so happens that these three steps for succeeding in achieving goals are the exact steps Katie Ledecky used on the road to Olympic gold. And so did Michael Phelps, winner of twenty-three gold medals over his career. And he has Adult ADD.

You may be wondering why I chose to highlight the success of Olympic athletes as a source of encouragement for adults with ADD. After all, some would argue that an Olympic athlete is the polar opposite of someone with ADD. Olympic athletes are prime specimens of discipline, focus, and single-minded dedication. Adults with ADD have difficulty with all three.

That is exactly the reason I chose Katie as a role model. In my opinion, learning how to manage the symptoms of Adult ADD is no less formidable than trying to win a gold medal in the Olympics. In some ways, it may even be more difficult—which is exactly why learning to set and keep appropriate goals is a key skill adults with ADD need if they ever hope to improve their symptoms.

Of course, no goal will be achieved without motivation. For that reason, I recommend that my clients choose something they truly feel is important to them at this moment in their lives. Do not try to be an angel and choose the equivalent of "achieving world peace," or even "making a million dollars." Stick with what you truly want—and are able—to achieve now. Having a hard time figuring out what you would like to accomplish? I often use meditation time to quiet my brain so I can think about what I truly want.

Once you have focused in on where your true motivation lies, I recommend moving forward along the lines of the following checklist:

- Prioritize your goals. This is extremely important. One of the drawbacks of Adult ADD, as I mentioned, is the desire to do everything, all the time. Instead, write down the goals you wish to achieve, and do a quick prioritization. Settle on no more than five key goals you would like to accomplish in the next year.

- Be realistic. Unrealistic expectations are the mother of despair, and despair is the mother of giving up. Don't be that guy (or gal). Start with something you believe you can achieve and work from there.

- Be specific. Make sure the goal is detailed, specific, and achievable. Running a 5K is doable. "Feed the poor" is not.

- Taste success, but taste complete success. A more effective long-term strategy is to break down goals into manageable steps. It also means choosing something you can accomplish quickly, even if it starts with just one day of making sure you leave the house with everything you need in the morning. One day builds into two, and soon enough a cycle of successful activity is being set in place. It may be that this is the only goal you work on for a month or more. Never mind. If you are successful in the beginning, you will be much more likely to continue.

- Reward every success. Here again, I encourage my clients to avoid trying to be heroes or angels. Some goals may be tedious. Obligations like doing the laundry, paying bills, being on time, etc., do not come with flashing neon lights. Building in a reward system is the fuel for your engine of success. This is more than a feel-good idea. It's backed by research on how the reward mechanism in our brains works. People with ADD often have lower levels of dopamine that those who do not have this condition. Dopamine is the neurotransmitter associated with reward and motivation. As a result of having lower levels of this chemical, adults with ADD often find themselves starving for stimulation and reward. Given this reality, I tell my clients to work with their biology, rather than fighting it. If you need rewards and excitement, then give yourself rewards and excitement. Just tie it to the achievement of a short-term goal. If you want to run a marathon, start with running a 5K and reward yourself with a trip or a new item when you accomplish this goal.

- Just do it. This last point is very important. Just get started. One of the drawbacks of Adult ADD is procrastination. Don't overthink your goal setting, especially in the beginning. Just choose something you can get started on, and get started on it.

I find that my clients are most successful when they combine this checklist with the support of an outside "accountability coach." Just like Katie Ledecky worked day in, day out with her swimming coach, adults with ADD should not be ashamed to draw on the resources of a trusted friend, life coach, or therapist.

I used my own advice when I came up with the idea to build an online course for adults with ADD. First I came up with a realistic plan. Then I cleared the calendar from doing any other big goals. Then I found a few consultants to help externalize the motivation. I then built a mastermind group from a few friends I trust, working on their own businesses. We agreed to meet once a week to monitor our progress and motivate one other. I told my group about my long-term and short-term goals and worked hard to meet them for our weekly calls. On occasion, I failed to meet my short-term goals, but I simply renegotiated the agreements and continued on with my plan. I broke my shoulder snowboarding, which set me back, but I reset new goals and finally accomplished my course.

Once a person gets in the habit of working within this system, it becomes much easier to manage the symptoms of Adult ADD. As Wayne Gretsky would have put it: Go ahead. Take the shot!

Daily Checklist

1. Set an alarm at 10:30 p.m. to wind down before bed.
2. Buy a water dispenser, and place it nearby.
3. Read *The Zone Diet* by Barry Sears to learn how to regulate glucose levels.
4. Find an exercise plan that is interesting, easy to start, and social.
5. Medication can work for focus and attention, but therapy or coaching is the best long-term solution.
6. Find a meditation center to learn how to meditate.
7. Download the On Second Thought app, and use the "Undo Send" feature in e-mail.
8. When angry, imagine a box around you, and exhale all the air in your lungs.
9. Join a mastermind group to avoid toxic shame and fear of failure.
10. Find a personal and spiritual-growth community that offers you helpful feedback and caring support.
11. Politely decline large projects or tasks where success is not guaranteed. Follow through on small ones to build trust.
12. Say "No" out loud to yourself when you find yourself doing "one more thing."
13. Have a phrase ready ("I would love to, but...") to use when someone asks you to do something.
14. Read *Getting Things Done* and *Zen To Done*. Also, use the Pomodoro Technique.

15. Filter a new e-mail address you set up to go into a new "@Followup" folder. Then bcc yourself using this e-mail address on all important e-mails that require follow-up.

16. Externalize the motivation by hiring a coach, working on a team, or setting time-bound goals. Don't "should" on yourself by thinking you can do it alone.

17. Accept your weaknesses, and delegate difficult tasks.

18. Ask yourself if you're a "square peg in a round hole." If so, it's time to consider a new job or career.

19. Manage the open loops in your life by limiting new ones and working with a buddy, partner, or coach to externalize the motivation to close open loops.

20. Set one new goal that is realistic, time-bound, and specific. Write it down, make it public, and break it into small steps.

Daily Quiz

What makes a goal successful?

a) Breaking the goal down into smaller doable steps.
b) Be specific, achievable, time-based, realistic and public.
c) Finding a friend to set the goal with and working together.

Correct Answer: a, b, and c

Day 27 & 28: Weekend Review

Procrastination

Procrastination is a complex phenomenon that requires careful analysis. Do you procrastinate because you feel you "should" do something, even though you hate it or it's not in your wheelhouse of talents? Or do you feel like you're forcing a square peg in a round hole, doing tasks or a job for which you're not well suited? If so, perhaps the problem is not procrastination, but rather that you're simply doing the wrong job. Time to find a new line of work better suited to your unique talents. If you absolutely must do the task or job, set goals and "externalize the motivation" by finding an accountability partner or coach to motivate you to get the job done.

Don't Should on Yourself

Forcing yourself to do something you don't like or are not good it is called "shoulding on yourself." Accept your weaknesses and limitations and delegate or decline these tasks. If you can't do either, ask for help.

Square Peg, Round Hole

Are you struggling in a job or with tasks you can't seem to complete? Is motivation a real deficit for you? If so, you might be a square peg in a round hole—out of place in the wrong job. Find a new job that suits your strengths and doesn't highlight your weaknesses on daily basis.

Closing the Loops

Open loops are unfinished tasks and jobs. Be mindful about opening new loops and work with a coach or accountability partner to close existing loops.

Setting Goals

Without goals it is easy to lose motivation. Set long- and short-term goals; make them public; write them down; and work with a partner, team, or coach to help make your dreams come true.

DAY 29
My Story, Part 1

oday I'm going to walk you through my own transformation with Adult ADD and how I overcame some hideous failures and mistakes to become the business owner and man I am today.

I grew up in New Haven, Connecticut, and attended public school until seventh grade. It wasn't until sixth grade that I actually felt I was at a disadvantage. In middle school, they divided up the class of one hundred students into four levels: A, B, C, and D. Guess what level I was in? Level C. It was pretty obvious that those kids in levels A and B were bright and studious. My class, being level C, was just average. When one of my friends moved from C to B, I really began to wonder what made the difference between "just average" and "better than average." Was it turning in homework on time? Or getting higher scores on tests? Regardless, the feeling of not being enough began to grow inside me and was especially pronounced when my older sister and younger brother ascended to level A in their respective years. But since I was getting by, no one thought to evaluate me for

ADD. And it was the eighties, a decade when understanding of ADHD was just in its infancy.

In seventh grade, I entered private school, and the pressure increased, correlating with a decrease in my grades. The workload was significant, and my desire to complete the work non-existent. I, like many with ADD, waited until the last minute on Sunday night to begin to even think about homework. I was a strong C student with occasional dips into the D range, but I enjoyed high school and excelled at wrestling and lacrosse. When I was accepted to Emory University, a school with neither a wrestling or lacrosse team, my college counselor was so surprised she invited me to give a talk, "How to Get into the College of Your Choice," to the parents of rising seniors. My answer: Apply to as many schools as possible, and cross your fingers.

College was worse for me than high school. I found out that being in a fraternity was way more fun than going to class. And taking a road trip to Florida midweek sure beat getting up at 8:00 a.m. for a statistics class. My parents and I blamed my poor performance on my social life and not having the right focus. Yet other friends seemed to be able to balance the two and succeed in school. Why couldn't I? I would go to the library but quickly get bored and fall asleep on the comfy couches near the stacks. My college years were some of the best of my life and some of the worst if you consider my school performance, lack of focus, and inability to follow through. Needless to say, I barely graduated. I dragged myself out of college in four years, scarred, but really no more aware about the reason for my lack of motivation and inability to focus and follow through.

After college, I applied and was accepted to Princeton University to teach in Korea through a program they offer called "Princeton in Asia." Of course, I applied late, and there were no spots until one opened up when someone dropped out. I got lucky again.

Living and working in Korea was the best year of my life. I was excited about teaching English and loved exploring the country. Creating lesson plans was torture for me, but I made up for it by bringing fun games into the classroom. I noticed, though, that some of the other teachers' classes consistently had more students signed up. I heard through the grapevine from a student that "if you really wanted to learn to speak English, the other teachers' lessons were better organized." While organization was not my strong suit, I engaged easily with my students and genuinely cared about them. This came through, and the students who did attend my classes were loyal. As the year came to a close, I decided to visit Japan. Missing my flight afforded me the chance to sit next to a Japanese businessman. We struck up a conversation, and he invited me to homestay with his family for a few months in southern Japan. I jumped at the chance to move to Japan. A few months turned into two years as I taught English and studied Japanese at a local YMCA.

My experience in Asia was life changing. I had to deal with many challenges living on my own in a strange country. There were many missteps, screwups, and lost opportunities, but I thrived in a foreign land, which supported my self-esteem immeasurably. Returning home was not easy. Culture shock and lack of jobs made my life difficult. I wanted to work in television and moved from Maryland, where I was staying with my parents, to New York City. I found a rent-stabilized apartment and settled in—along with the mice that inhabited my rent-stabilized apartment. But such is life in New York City.

For the next six years, I worked in a variety of television and new media positions. But the universe or G-d or the role of the dice was never really in my favor. I really was not cut out for the politics of business or the lack of autonomy when working in a large corporation. I didn't really want my boss's job or my boss's boss's job, and this lack of motivation showed. Being fired for my ADD symptoms and living off unemployment showed me that I needed a change and that I was better suited for something completely different. After months of anxious decision making, I decided to go back to school to become a psychologist. This was not a snap decision but one done in consultation with friends and family, whom I finally listened to, as they knew me best. It was hard to see myself in any way other than the "tech mogul" persona that I had created for myself, but my mother especially helped me see that I was probably better suited for a helping profession like psychotherapy. I had majored in psychology and enjoyed the learning, so this was a realistic career for me. In time, I came to realize my true calling and applied for graduate school in psychology.

Stay tuned for the rest of this story tomorrow.

DAY 30

My Story, Part 2

I knew that I needed external motivation to reach my goal of becoming a psychologist, and so I thought that graduate school was the perfect road. It would be a hard journey, but I liked the idea of a long-term goal with short-term milestones along the way. I was also hopeful that the structure of graduate school would provide a path to success.

Once in school, I excelled because I was motivated about the subject matter and excited about the learning. I was finally a round peg in a round hole. There was also fear, which served as a great motivator, as I felt that this was my last chance at a successful life. But I still struggled with time management, especially with being late to class and events.

A professor recommended a personal growth community called the ManKind Project, a men's group with centers all over the world. Accountability is paramount in this organization, and I soon learned that being late was not acceptable. Through this group, I understood that time management is relationship management, and showing up five minutes late is a direct breach of trust and accountability in the relationship. If I wanted to remain

150

respected and connected to others, I needed to be on time. I didn't master this in one day, but over a few years working with this group, I became accountable and one who respected the time of others.

Leaving school left me back in the wild, so to speak, without the support structure of professors and school staff. I had the goal of opening my own practice after receiving my license. But struggling to do everything by myself was a huge mistake I made early and often. I quickly realized that I shouldn't do everything and that I needed to delegate. I learned to hire others and to allow experts (i.e., accountants) to do what I couldn't and shouldn't do. Hiring my assistant, Rachelle, on upwork.com was a game changer for me. She didn't have Adult ADD and was very detail oriented, and thus, by proxy, I appeared detailed oriented. My business starting flourishing once I realized I shouldn't do everything. I didn't make a substantial profit until after I acknowledged that I needed help and hired Rachelle. She is that vital to my business.

I improved the quality of my client contact dramatically by using the e-mail systems outlined in this book: getting back to clients immediately, even with a short response, and following up with clients using the @followup folder and bcc'ing myself using a special e-mail address on important e-mails. I downloaded Right Inbox and used Inbox by Gmail to further manage my e-mail flow. I used Google Calendar to stay on top of appointments, which was also a lifesaver. And I employed a do-it-now strategy for dealing with logistical information. If a client canceled, I immediately deleted the appointment from Google Calendar. I found that if I didn't do it immediately, it was lost in the fog of time.

I created the impression that I was available for clients, and I was—too much in the beginning. I eventually learned to set boundaries regarding the length of the sessions and when I would return calls after hours. In the beginning, I lacked confidence in my therapy, which is not unusual, so I would go over time, thinking this would help. It only made me more tired and confused the clients. So I learned to set boundaries, which created a healthier work atmosphere for me and for the client.

As mentioned previously, when I decided to build this course, I knew that I could not do it alone. I needed an accountability partner to keep me focused and motivated on my goals. I found two friends, also building their businesses, and we set up a small mastermind group and had weekly check-ins about the progress of our projects. This has worked very well, and I've grown closer to these individuals.

Now I am at the point where I would like to see fewer clients and focus more on my online business. At the moment I am doing both and working more hours than I would like. My short-term goal is to delegate some of my clients to a new therapist I hired for my practice. This will support my colleague's growth and allow me to work more on the courses. I have also hired online course consultants along the way to externalize my motivation and keep me focused on my goal.

There will continue to be hiccups in my road of life. I'm confident, though, that with my ADD under control and with the support I have created around me, I am on the right path.

I hope you enjoy this and future courses. It is my hope that this course changes the trajectory of your life, leading you to new and exciting places.

If you would like to learn more about Adult ADD, check out our thirty day online-learning program called the Adult ADD Solution. To learn more about this program, go to adultaddsolution.com. Get a 10% discount with the code: **add10**

21323409R00089

Made in the USA
Columbia, SC
16 July 2018